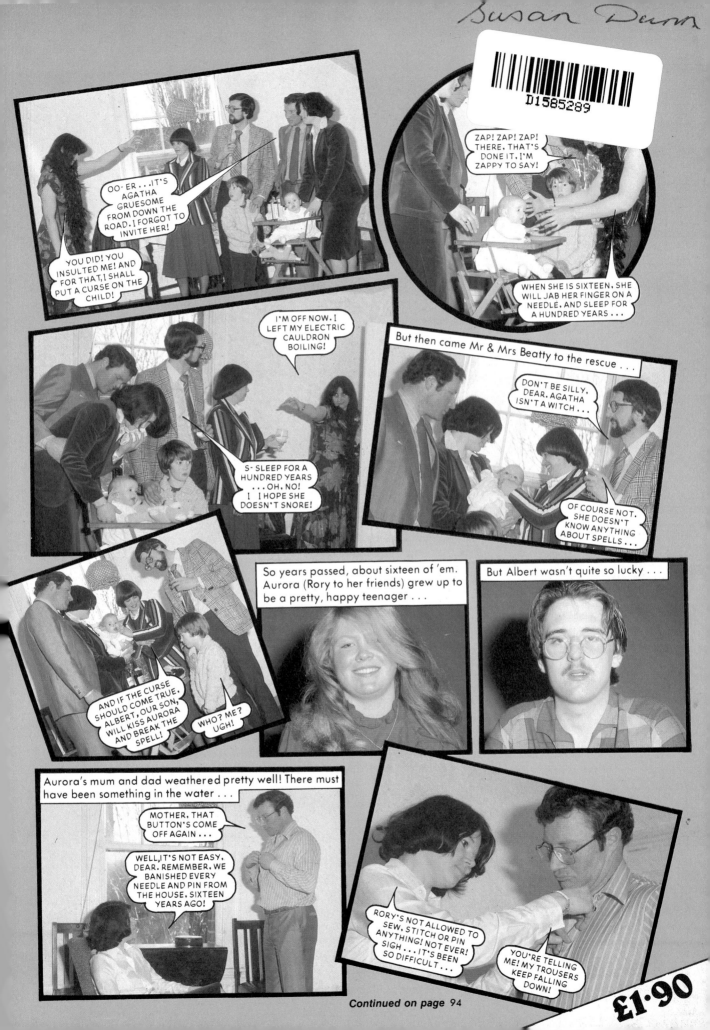

Continued on page 94

CONTENTS

FEATURES

FUN

SHORT STORIES

FASHION

ED QUARTERS

Hi! Welcome to the second Patches Annual. I just know for a fact you're going to love it. Well, it's a lot like me – good to look at, witty, fun, sparkling with life . . . I could go on, but modesty forbids! (Zzzz . . . – The Patches office).

Don't forget, Patches – and me! – are around every week to brighten up your life. Order us every Friday from your newsagent!

Love, The Ed

Printed and Published in Great Britain by D. C. Thomson & Co., Ltd., 185 Fleet Street, London EC4A 2HS. © D. C. Thomson & Co., Ltd., 1982.
ISBN 085116 2479

DON'T BE A DRIP!

You look out of the window and your heart sinks – it's pouring with rain! But don't despair, because Patches is here to brighten up your life! Try any one of these ideas to chase the blues away . . .

1. Dress up in your bright red/yellow mac and wellies and go for a paddle in the puddles.

2. Get out your mum's box of old photos and have a good laugh. Then sort out your own photos and fill your album up.

3. Call your friends and invite them over to your place. Then spend the day making each other up and changing your hairstyles.

4. Get out that box of paints that's been lying at the back of the cupboard and try your hand at painting.

5. Either get some henna or a toner or rinse and put it on your hair. Leave it on as long as possible and you'll never go unnoticed again!

6. Tidy your bedroom and re-arrange it at the same time. This might sound totally boring but it will pass the time and you'll be amazed at how good your room looks.

7. This is a follow-on from number six. Look under your bed and you'll find everything that's been lost since last year. Count all the items.

8. Put on your youngest-looking clothes and go to a children's matinee. Join in the jokes and laughter and eat plenty of ice-cream.

9. Raid your mum's sewing basket and make a cushion out of scraps of fabric. Then you can get rid of all your old, holey tights when you stuff it!

10. Search high and low and get all your old copies of Patches together. Then cover them with a colourful binder using bright cardboard, glue and a bit of imagination.

11. Bake some "character" biscuits — gingerbread men, snowmen, animals — as many different shapes as possible.

12. Go through all your records, separating the albums and singles; clean them well and catalogue them.

13. Go through all your clothes to check if they're in good condition or whether they could do with a wash. If there are any buttons loose, hems coming down, etc. — mend them!

14. Play some good, fast records and exercise to them. Bend as much as possible — really make those lazy muscles work.

15. Practise with your make-up in front of the mirror. Try to be professional — blend all those colours in well, and remember to use brushes!

16. If you've got long hair, put it into as many tiny plaits as you can and leave them in for as long as possible. When you take them out, your hair'll be lovely and wavy.

17. Get a simple bread recipe and make it. Once you've done the dough you could use it for rolls. Make as many unusual shapes as possible — plaiting, knotting the dough, etc. They look great when they're baked!

18. Go through all your old magazines and cut out all your favourite pictures. Paste them to a large sheet of card or stiff paper and hang it on your wall. The collage effect'll be terrific!

19. Write some poetry. But don't just stick to soppy love poems — try as many different kinds as possible.

20. Get out all your favourite postcards and birthday cards and cover the top of an old chest-of-drawers or table with them, then put clear Contact on top. Then stand back and admire it.

21. Do up your face like Toyah. Make it as colourful and outrageous as possible — then clean it off!

22. Write down all the little things you need to do like watering the plants, clean-ing your make-up brushes, hemming your trousers, then tear it up and relax!

23. Read a book.

24. Give yourself a face-pack using the white of an egg and then try to smile. Watch the cracks!

25. Draw a self-portrait but be honest! Try to get it as true to life as possible.

26. Make a chart and write everyone's birthdays on it so you don't forget them.

27. Make up your bed so tightly that you have to squeeze into it at night.

28. Write down the names of everyone you know — you'll be surprised at the length of the list.

29. Crawl everywhere! Everyone'll think you've gone mad!

30. Count the raindrops on your window. Then make bets with your friends on the raindrops running down the pane. First to the window-sill's the winner.

31. Read through all your old diaries and Valentine cards.

32. Go for a walk in the rain with your boyfriend and huddle very close together under one small umbrella.

33. Raid the attic — but take supplies of food and Coke. You never know when you'll emerge again . . .

34. Have the longest bath in history. Take everything you need into the bathroom with you — bath oil, soap, shampoo and talc. Include sandwiches, biscuits, a flask of tea — then lie back and have a tremendous soak!

35. Paint your toenails electric blue or flashing apricot!

36. Concoct your own "rain cake" and bake it every rainy day.

37. Go for a sauna.

38. Make an "Oxfam Pile." Go through all your clothes and put the ones you never wear to one side. Some-one'll be grateful for them.

39. Sort through your make-up bag, throwing out all the yukky, horrible shades and clean your bag. Keep the lipsticks, though.

40. Now you can melt down all those old lipsticks and make a new shade.

41. Phone up all your friends and tell them to put on bright macs and wellies, then go out singing in the rain!

42. Clean the inside of your bedroom window and watch the outside being cleaned for you by the rain.

43. Write to all the people you haven't written to for ages.

44. Find a quiet corner and meditate.

45. Get out all the soppy records you own and have a good weep. See if you can beat the raindrops with your tears . . .

46. Clean every single pair of shoes you own.

47. Wear bright yellow clothes and sunglasses and pretend you're in a tropical heatwave.

48. Get your old T-shirts together and dye them bright colours.

49. Find the biggest jigsaw puzzle in the house and do it.

50. Curl up on the settee and have a nice doze. Pretend you're the cat!

STARGAZING!

PISCES (Feb. 19-Mar. 20)

You are the dreamer of the zodiac, forever planning for a rosy future, then being disappointed when you realise that you can't always have your own way. In the first three months of the year, you'll be meeting many new friends and taking up a whole range of new interests, some of which are bound to bring you good luck. Spend some time studying before Easter comes round and you may be proud of the results this summer. Romance blossoms for you in autumn.

ARIES (Mar. 21-April 20)

Keep a strong check on that famous, fiery Arian temper, especially when dealing with members of your family, otherwise you could miss out on something important. This summer, you'll find yourself faced with an agonising decision concerning two guys you like very much, but remember, good looks aren't always the best guide to what the person is really like. It seems likely that you'll be spending more time than usual with your family in the early months of the year, but there's a happy reason for it.

TAURUS (April 21-May 20)

Whatever you do in connection with work or school will turn out extremely well, especially around May or June when you could receive a prize for a project you've been working on. Try to be a little less self-centred in your approach, or you might miss one or two very important chances by scaring people off. A romance which starts around the time of your birthday could turn out to be all you've ever dreamed of, but don't start making long-term plans just yet!

GEMINI (May 21-June 20)

You can be quite selfish at times, especially when it comes to making arrangements with friends — you want it all your own way! But watch out for a troublemaker who might put your friends against you because of this. Your great adaptability and love for spontaneous outings will ensure this summer really takes off. Remember that guy who caused a lot of heartache some months ago? Well, it seems like he's going to play an important part in your social life this year, whether you like it or not!

CANCER (June 21-July 21)

Keeping a secret from your parents will cause more trouble than it's worth, so come clean and you'll be suprised at how helpful and understanding they are. A friendship which starts on a very light-hearted basis could turn into a serious relationship, but there will be a few problems to overcome in the early stages. You might get a rare chance to travel to a foreign country, but not necessarily for a holiday — do all you can to make use of this opportunity.

LEO (July 22-August 21)

The first half of the year will be very busy, but there might be so many promises to fulfill that your social life will have to take second place — not a pleasing situation for a fun-loving Leo. However, the summer always seems to bring out the best in you, not least because you are the true sun-worshipper of the zodiac, and romance should make this a time to remember. Something which concerns your future career will be discussed deeply towards the end of the year.

With our special Patches guide to your stars in 1983, you just can't go wrong! Here, we give you a preview of what to expect from the year ahead . . .

VIRGO (August 22-Sept. 21)

Something you wouldn't even have dreamed of doing before will occur to you as a good idea around March, and the result could have a very deep affect on your relationship with a special guy. This doesn't mean it will be for the worse, just that there will be changes evident. Your pride could prevent you from taking a chance in a competition this summer, which would be a pity as that's going to be one of the luckiest times of the year for you.

LIBRA (Sept. 22-Oct. 22)

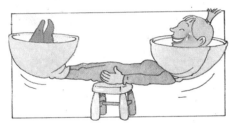

You should guard against being too easy-going with your mates or you'll just be taken for granted, when what you need to do is be a little more selfish and give some time to personal interests. There are some quite dramatic changes forecast for you, especially in the spring, when you'll have more cash than usual and you'll be able to make decisions about your future with confidence. Romance is linked with someone from your past and you might resume a relationship with an old boyfriend.

SCORPIO (Oct. 23 - Nov. 21)

A promise someone made to you a long time ago will be fulfilled by February, when you'd almost given up hope of seeing that person again. There's a once-in-a-lifetime event forecast for July, so make sure you're looking your best by getting in trim this spring, and with the extra cash coming your way in April you'll be able to splash out on something expensive this summer. Some very good news will reach you from abroad in late autumn.

SAGITTARIUS (Nov. 22-Dec. 20)

For a long time people have been holding you back from something you really want to do, but this year you'll find all that has changed. No-one's going to stand in your way, especially where your hobbies and personal interests are concerned. You have the determination to succeed and you know you will! There's a strong link with people from overseas, especially around September, and you may even be travelling to meet them.

CAPRICORN (Dec. 21-Jan. 20)

You've always lacked confidence to express how you feel to the people who matter to you, but a relationship you form this year with a Taurus or Virgo boy will help you overcome this shyness. Socially, you will be playing hostess once or twice in the first couple of months of the year, when someone in the family springs a surprise on you. Around autumn, you should find you have a little more money to spend, but keep a check on that impulsive streak of yours!

AQUARIUS (Jan. 21-Feb. 18)

The last thing an Aquarian could be accused of, is being conventional or boring, and this is what usually attracts all those admirers. But 1983 could bring a complete change of lifestyle to you, and it will all happen very suddenly. You're not exactly the most reliable of people, either, but the added responsibility will mean a quick change in your attitude, too — giving you more understanding to deal with emotional problems which arise around August or September.

WAKE UP!

If you thought "Sleepover" meant dashing into school at half-past nine, out of breath and trying to think of a good excuse for being a slob — now's the time to wake up and give your life a shake-up with the Patches guide to a slumberless sleepover — *everybody's* doing it . . .

SUCCESSFUL SLEEPOVERS!

HAVE you ever sat with your mates on a boring winter's afternoon and wondered what on earth you can do that weekend? You've got nowhere to go, nothing to do, and if you clubbed all your worldly goods together you'd end up with the princely sum of 90 pence. Wow . . .

Well, there *is* something you can do — you can have a sleepover. That doesn't mean curling up in bed and staying there all weekend — as if *any-one* would be lazy and unhealthy enough for that . . . All you'll need is a warm, comfy bedroom, a few mates and obliging parents (and if they're hard-of-hearing, so much the better).

Basically, having a sleepover means inviting a few friends over to your house to spend the night — we recommend anything from 3 to 5 of your mates, depending on how much room you have. Don't worry that you haven't got much space for everyone to spread out in — your mates won't mind curling up in a sleeping bag on the floor. You won't get to sleep for talking all night, anyway.

FRIENDS

First of all, make sure you only ask a group of girls who all get on well together.

You don't want one of them shouting, "I'm not staying here with *her* all night," and stomping off into the darkness, with you in pursuit!

So now you've got together a good bunch of mates, and round they all come to your place . . .

MUSIC

If any of your friends has a particularly good collection of records or tapes, this can be her contribution to the sleepover — ask her to bring them along so you'll have plenty of good background music to get everyone in the right mood.

But as well as listening to the music and joining in, you could arrange with your friends that you'll all bring maybe three or four albums that you're tired of, and set up your own swap shop. All you do is put all the albums into a "pool," draw lots for who goes first, then keep passing them round, for everyone to choose one at a time. And you'll all have a new pile of albums — for nothing!

BOOKS 'N' MAGS

The same can go for any books or magazines you have lying around — tell everyone to bring along some old paperbacks and mags they have, and you can have great fun looking through them, borrowing the ones you want, and arranging to swap with the others later.

Or you could try out all those daft quizzes in old magazines (you'll find some great ones in old copies of Patches, of course!). Or why not stage your own pop quiz — the winner gets the best album in the pile, before you start drawing lots for them!

NEW LOOKS FOR OLD

Ever wondered what you'd look like in a new style of clothes or with a new hairdo?

Your sleepover's a good time to find out — and you'll get the honest opinion of your best mates, without going out to school wondering if you really look as weird as you feel!

If everybody brings along three or four extra outfits, you'll all have lots of different things to try on and co-ordinate — you may end up wanting to swap these, too!

It's quite likely that at least one of your crowd is going to be "good with hair" — so why not set up your own little salon and give each other a new hair-style? Or tell everyone to bring along all their old bits and pieces of make-up, nail polish, etc., and really give yourselves a "new look."

DANCING

Been doing the same old shuffle on the disco floor for the last two years?

Well, there's probably a disco champion among your mates who'd love to help you with your dancing technique, or lack of it! Even if none of you quite makes next year's Disco Dancing Finals, you'll have a lot of giggles — and it's better than trying out a new routine on the disco floor and wondering why no-one ever asks you to dance!

FOOD

Once your mum and dad are safely in bed, you can get down to the serious business of eating.

If you really don't have any cash to spare, you can always raid your mum's larder and create some weird and wonderful dishes with the help of some tins of beans, a few sausages, and some cheese.

But if you do have a little money, why not club together in advance and buy in your midnight feast? You could really indulge yourselves and have a Junk Food Jamboree — just make a list of all the delicious, tempting junk food that you secretly love and, just for once, treat yourself to the lot!

HAVE A NATTER

The thing you'll *really* enjoy about having all your mates round is the chat! And the nicest thing of all about having a sleepover is that you don't have to say goodbye, and rush off for the last bus, just when the conversation's getting interesting.

Once you're all ready for bed, you can sit in the semi-darkness and tell stories. Something spooky, some weird coincidence, some frightening experience — you'll all have either had one yourself or know of someone who has.

Don't go to sleep on that, though — you'll all have nightmares and end up quaking with fear at the sound of one of your mates breathing in your ear. If ghost stories leave you a bit jumpy, try telling jokes — it'll soon make you feel better!

Or one of you start a sentence with a few words, like, "The last boy I went out with . . ." the next person has to repeat it exactly and add on her bit, the next person does the same and adds on her bit, and so on, and you're out of the game if you make a mistake or can't think of anything to add immediately it's your turn. It gets quite interesting if you all agree that the bits you add will actually be the truth!

These are all just some of the things you can do at your sleepover — but once you and your friends get together, you're bound to have lots of other ideas. One word of warning, though — don't decide to hold your sleepover on an evening when you've got something important to do the next day — 'cos one thing's certain — you won't get much sleeping done — Goodnight!

ON THE WRITE TRACK!

From now on, you'd better think twice before you sign your name to anything! Why? Well, from just a glimpse of your handwriting, other people can learn more about you than even *you* know! Mystified? Fascinated? Then read on . . .

Aye, Aye!

First, write "I am crazy doing this!" on a scrap of paper. Now study your capital "I," then look at the examples below and decide which one yours is closest to.

If it's a straight line (a), then you're a clear thinker and like to be creative. *If you have loops to your capital "I"* (b), you're a bit of a show-off, and never happier than when you're making people laugh. *If it's sharp at the top* (c), it means you tend to be a sarcastic, sometimes rather aggressive, person, and *an "I" that is rounded and large* (d), indicates a good sense of humour.

If your "I" is particularly large (e), you're likely to have a very high opinion of yourself, but *if it's smaller than the rest of your handwriting* (f), you're a bit too modest for your own good!

Hair by Layla d'Angelo for Ellis Helen.

Loopy Letters

Now study the lower loops on your "g" and "y" letters. *If they're long and full* (a), it means you're a very energetic kind of person and always on the go, and *if they're a straight line down* (b), you're very direct, regularly speaking your mind and dislike wafflers of any kind!

Small, insignificant loops (c), suggest a tendency to be lazy, and *long, narrow loops* (d), reveal the opposite — you're full of nervous energy and find it difficult to relax. *Large, exaggerated loops* (e), mean that you have a very vivid imagination — you take a sneaky delight in telling tall stories to gain attention! *Angular and triangular loops* (f), reveal a tendency to be argumentative and aggressive.

The Long and the Short

Now have a look at the whole sentence. Would you say your writing is large or small, or pretty average, really? And are the spaces between the words large or practically non-existent? If you're in doubt, compare yours with the handwriting of a few friends — it's much easier to judge that way.

If your handwriting is large, it means you're a very emotional kind of person and a bit of a show-off at the same time — you love being in the limelight and making your views known to an admiring audience!

If it's small, you're more of an introvert, preferring to do a lot of *thinking*, rather than going out and *doing* things.

Large spaces between your words suggest a rather shy person with a tendency to be reserved, especially in the company of people you're not too sure of.

Small spaces mean that you're a bit of an extrovert, and very open with people, whether they're close friends or strangers.

Now have a look at your small "a" and "o" letters. *If they're closed,* as in the first example, you tend to be a little secretive, which isn't such a bad thing sometimes! And *if you leave them open,* you're a bit of a gossip, who absolutely adores talking!

All Ship-Shape!

And now for the general style of your handwriting. Take a look at the following four examples — we've labelled them *round and regular, thread-like, angular,* and *softly rounded.* See which style your handwriting resembles, and find out just what it means.

Round and Regular: Your "n" and "m" letters are rather like arcades — very rounded at the top — and this means you have a habit of keeping your thoughts to yourself. We're sorry to have to tell you this, but you also have a bit of a lazy streak to your nature!

Thread-like: This writing looks as if a spider has crawled across the page, leaving a trail behind it, and this reveals that you tend to be rather evasive when it comes to showing your true feelings. You're anything *but* an open book, which can be a bit frustrating for your friends at times. However, you manage to use this to your favour in that you can often get exactly what you want without seeming to do so!

Angular: This very definitely angular style of handwriting suggests that you're a very down-to-earth, decisive type of person. However, you tend to get a little bit aggressive and bossy when things aren't quite to your liking. (Take care you don't frighten off all those lovely-but-shy blokes!)

Softly-rounded: This very gentle style of handwriting tends to reflect your personality in that you're a very gentle kind of person — easy-going, generous (sometimes to a fault!) and very friendly.

So there you are – some invaluable tips on handwriting analysis! Try it out amongst your mates – if you dare!

One day in the life of ....

Meet one of our favourite musicians. He's "modelled" on Peter-Paul. In fact . . . it's none other than PP himself! Peter-Paul has done loads of Patches' covers and fashion pages, and now he's springing into the world of music! He's already made a single, an EP and LP's — and he's still modelling! He let us look-in on one day in his busy life . . .

8 a.m.: the joys of jogging — and bending, and stretching!

8.30 a.m.: shower, vegetarian breakfast — in that order, please!

12.30 p.m.: pre-arranged photo session with James Jordan, Fashion photographer at Smiles Studio. Saying cheese!

5 p.m.: PP the musician arrives at recording studio; work on my solo LP Musical Adventure involved using everything from toys to telephones for sound effects; but first I phone model agency to check on any modelling booked for next day.

PETER-PAUL

10.00 a.m.: haired along to Sissors, in The Kings Rd., where I'm a house model.

10.30 a.m.: mad as a hatter!

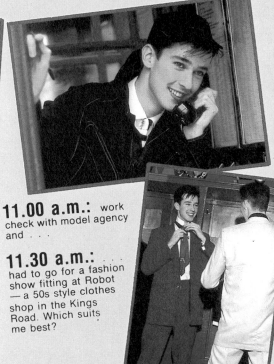

11.00 a.m.: work check with model agency and . . .

11.30 a.m.: . . . had to go for a fashion show fitting at Robot — a 50s style clothes shop in the Kings Road. Which suits me best?

11.20 p.m.: at last — bed-time! But also book-time!

Peter-Paul's day is busy to the very end! We just left him burrowed in his bedclothes and book — but not before he sent goodnight kisses to all Patches' readers!

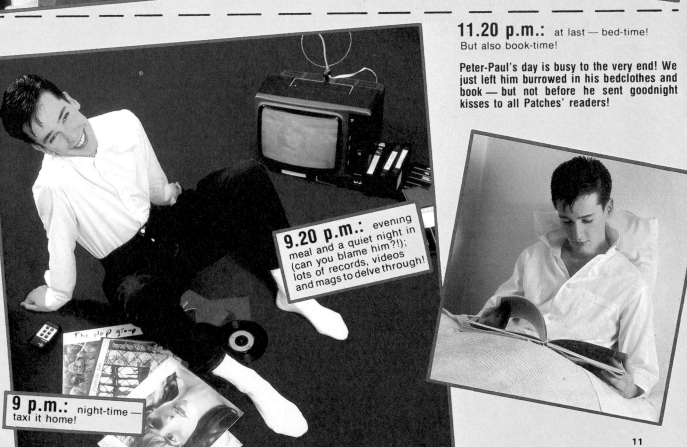

9.20 p.m.: evening meal and a quiet night in (can you blame him?!); lots of records, videos and mags to delve through!

9 p.m.: night-time — taxi it home!

FRAMED

Pin-ups have changed ever so slightly through the years.

Socrates — a great Greek philosopher. Seemed like a nice boy!

Humphrey Bogart, who starred in many classics, including "Casablanca."

Errol Flynn was everyone's heart-throb once upon a time!

Clark Gable starring in "Never Let Me Go."

Bing Crosby in full song!

Fred Astaire and his famous dancing feet wowed the world!

The very boyish-looking Frank Sinatra.

A rather sultry-looking Cary Grant.

Charlton Heston in "El Cid."

AT LAST!

Here's the pick of the bunch for your delectation and delight!

The ever-popular Paul Newman.

Marlon Brando relaxing between scenes in "Julius Caesar."

Dean Martin starring in "Ocean's Eleven."

The amazing James Dean.

Mean and moody Clint Eastwood.

David Cassidy thrilled everyone with his acting and singing.

Peter Frampton made lots of girls swoon!

Remember Donny Osmond and his famous brothers?

Adam Ant — a firm favourite today.

WHAT A BEAST!

HEY, did you know that in saying dogs are your favourite animal and that you can't stand snakes, you're revealing the innermost secrets of your personality to everyone within ear-shot? Pretty scary, eh? But it's perfectly true!

Everyone has a special liking for a certain kind of animal. And — wait for it! — this preference can actually show what kind of person you are!

Fancy trying it out for yourself? Well, choose your favourite animal from the ones we've shown here, and then find out how you shape up in the personality stakes. We bet you'll be quite surprised by the results!

The Dog

You are a steady, reliable kind of person, with a well-balanced attitude to life. At the same time, though, you are aware of certain faults in yourself, and are very tolerant of faults in others, accepting your friends just as they are.

You place great importance on friendship and loyalty, as human relationships are your number one priority.

The Leopard

You tend to be a little uncertain of yourself at times and you may find it difficult to relax totally in company, except with people you are really sure of.

That streak of pride in your nature is reluctant to let you make a fool of yourself, so when faced with a decision, you'll weigh up all sides extremely carefully before finally reaching any conclusion about what you should do.

You're totally reliable in a crisis and — believe it or not — most people have a secret admiration for you and probably wish they could be more like you!

The Horse

Freedom is the thing you value most in your life, and woe betide anyone who tries to tie you down. You rush from one idea to the next at a mind-boggling rate, and you're happiest when you're doing things that are wildly and wonderfully different!

But at least you've sat down long enough to read this feature — well, everyone needs a break sometimes . . . even you!

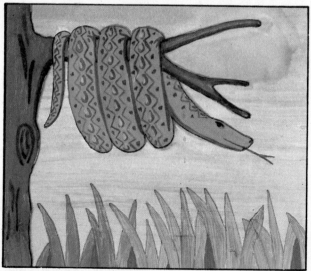

The Snake

People who don't know you too well might think you an extremely confident and rather aggressive type of person, and therefore are a little intimidated by you!

Only your closest friends will know that underneath this display of confidence, lurks a very warm-hearted and generous person, who is far from being totally sure of herself!

Other people's opinions of you matter a lot, but remember that you can't possibly please all of the people all of the time!

The Elephant

Most of the time, you're a calm and quiet type of person, but as your mates will have found out, this doesn't mean people can take advantage of your good nature and get away with it!

You have this amazing hot temper that can flare up so quickly, you leave folk wondering what on earth hit 'em! It's lucky for other people that your outbursts usually die down as quickly as they flared up!

The Panda

You're a very practical kind of person and you can usually be relied upon for your commonsense. But this doesn't mean you don't go weak at the knees every time you catch a glimpse of someone you really fancy!

You're fond of the simple pleasures in life, and you're at your happiest when you're with people you love and who love you.

The Eagle

Being rather shy and introverted, it's often very hard for other people to get to know the real you, although once they do, you usually have a friend for life.

Although you'd like to be more open with others, you're actually a bit scared to show them what you're really like, in case they don't like what they see! So get off the defensive and confide in people a bit more — you'll probably find they respond really warmly to you.

The Dolphin

You're the complete extrovert in every sense of the word — full of life, extremely talkative, and the life and soul of every party (which naturally makes you very popular at party-time!).

But take care that you don't become so involved in yourself that you ignore the feelings of those who are less boisterous than you. Shyer boys may find you a bit overwhelming, so beware of frightening them off!

On the whole, though, you get a lot of fun out of life and are very rarely bored — or boring!

If you've got a few hours to spare and nothing special to fill them with, read on. We'll show you how to make some fantastic beauty products at gorgeously inexpensive prices!

Clean And Simple

If you want a cheap, natural cleanser there're plenty of ingredients in your kitchen cupboards you could use to make your very own!

For gentle cleansers that will remove most make-up, put some almond oil or coconut oil on a wad of cotton wool and use this to cleanse your skin. These two are especially good.

Strawberry juice, warm milk or natural yoghurt are very good cleansers, too, but not as successful for heavy make-up. Here's a slightly more complicated recipe:

Cucumber Cleansing Milk

¼ cucumber
¼ pint milk

Extract the juice from the cucumber and add this to the milk, mixing well; this will keep for a few days in the fridge.

It's important to remember that any recipes which include edible items will not keep for long. It's best to make these recipes fresh daily or keep refrigerated for a couple of days.

Freshen Up!

Fresheners, toners and astringents are basically the same products but with different strengths. They help to close the pores and stimulate circulation.

Fresheners and toners **are for balanced or dry skins. There are lots of reasonably simple ingredients you can use. Try rubbing your skin with a slice of raw potato or add a teaspoonful of cider vinegar to 1½ cups of water. For a slightly more complex recipe, mix together 2 parts rose water to one part witch hazel and then bottle it.**

Astringents **are for oily and blemished skin. The above recipe can also be used but in different parts. Mix together 2 parts witch hazel to 3 parts rose water and shake it in a bottle.**

MAKE IT UP!

Make The Most Of Moisture!

For a simple moisturiser, cover your face with cucumber juice and after a couple of seconds blot it dry.

For slightly more work you can have a lovely Almond Moisturising Lotion. Take 30 g (1 oz.) almonds and 3 dl (½ pint) distilled water. Skin the almonds by dipping them in boiling then cold water and grind them to a powder. Add the distilled water drop by drop, continuing to blend until liquid is milky, then strain. Remember that this won't keep for long, though.

Handy! Handy!

Hands are constantly exposed and always on show, so you need to take extra care of them. To improve chapped hands, soak them each night in a bowl of cold or warm milk for 5 minutes. A slice of lemon, or its juice, will get rid of ingrained dirt. Here's a more complicated recipe for a hand cream.

Potato Hand Cream

2 potatoes, medium size
1 tablespoonful almond oil
1 tablespoonful glycerine
1 teaspoonful orange flower water

Cook and mash the potatoes, add the oil and finally the orange flower water. If the mixture is too thick, add more orange flower water. The end result is more of a paste than a cream. Apply to your hands, then rinse off after an hour.

Mouth To Mouth

Lip glosses are expensive, so why not try your own recipe? This is a balm to soothe chapped and dry lips.

1½ oz. (45 g) beeswax
1 oz. (30 g) honey
2 oz. (60 g) sesame oil.

Melt the beeswax in a double boiler, or heat-resistant container over a pan of boiling water; blend in the honey and then the oil, whisking until smooth.

For a lip gloss, take ½ teaspoonful beeswax and 2 tablespoonfuls of cocoa butter. Melt the wax and add the cocoa butter. When it cools it will solidify and you can then apply it with a lip brush.

Hair, Hair!

Shampoos are extremely important for beautiful hair and you can make some very effective ones yourself.

Egg Yolk Shampoo

2 egg yolks
1 cup warm water

Beat the yolks into the water, massage into the scalp and hair for 5 minutes; leave to soak in for 10 minutes. Rinse off.

Dear Roberto

THIS IS THE LAST LETTER I'LL EVER WRITE TO YOU, ROBERTO, AND I DON'T EVEN KNOW WHERE TO BEGIN . . .

I SUPPOSE I SHOULD START BY TELLING YOU HOW MUCH I LOVED YOU AND THE TIMES WE SPENT TOGETHER, LAST SUMMER . . .

Last year I'd gone to Spain with my mate, Beth, and . . .

WHAT DO YOU MEAN, YOU HAVEN'T GOT A ROOM FOR US? WE BOOKED IT MONTHS AGO!

I AM SORRY, SENORITA. IT APPEARS ZERE HAS BEEN A DOUBLE BOOKING.

ZE ROOM YOU SHOULD HAVE BEEN IN HAS ALREADY BEEN LET TO SOMEONE ELSE. IT IS UNFORTUNATE, BUT THESE THINGS HAPPEN.

THEN YOU'LL JUST HAVE TO GIVE US ANOTHER ROOM, WON'T YOU?

ALAS, SENORITA . . . ZE HOTEL IS COMPLETELY FULL. ONE OF ZE OTHER HOTELS MAY HAVE A VACANCY . . . BUT IN HIGH SEASON, IT IS UNLIKELY . . .

But just after we'd left the hotel we heard someone calling . . .

We went back to the hotel . . .

WELL . . . THANKS. AT LEAST OUR HOLIDAY'S NOT COMPLETELY RUINED!

DO NOT WORRY. JUAN AND I ARE ON HOLIDAY FROM MADRID, BUT WE HAVE A FRIEND HERE WHO WILL LET US SLEEP ON THE FLOOR OF HIS FLAT FOR THE NEXT TWO WEEKS.

And as we moved into the hotel they moved out . . .

MMM, THAT BOY ROBERTO'S NICE . . .

In our room . . .

IT WAS REALLY NICE OF THOSE BOYS TO GIVE UP THE ROOM FOR US, WASN'T IT, BETH?

YOU HAVEN'T STOPPED TALKING ABOUT THEM FOR THE LAST HALF HOUR. THEY REALLY MUST HAVE MADE AN IMPRESSION ON YOU!

OR AT LEAST ONE OF THEM DID!

SHE'S RIGHT. I REALLY FANCIED ROBERTO. BUT I DON'T SUPPOSE I'LL SEE HIM AGAIN . . .

But I did—the very next day on the beach . . .

HELLO, AGAIN, SENORITAS!

OH . . . HELLO, THERE!

ARE YOU SETTLED IN AT THE HOTEL?

YES, THANKS. HOW ABOUT YOU? ARE YOU OK AT YOUR FRIEND'S FLAT?

SI. HE HAS A VERY HARD FLOOR!

It seemed sort of natural to pair off— Roberto and I, and Beth and Juan.

DO NOT BELIEVE HIM IF HE TELLS YOU HIS ENGLISH IS POOR, BETH. HE SPEAKS VERY GOOD ENGLISH—ISN'T THAT SO, JUAN?

SI. MANCHESTER UNITED . . . KEVIN KEEGAN . . . !

We spent the whole day just wandering together—

... and when you kissed me I knew something magic had happened between us.

I WISH YOU DID NOT HAVE TO GO AWAY, JULIE.

OH, ROBERTO ... SO DO I. BUT TOMORROW'S MY LAST DAY. I—I'VE GOT TO GO BACK.

I was in tears as we said goodbye at the airport.

YOU WILL WRITE TO ME, WON'T YOU, ROBERTO?

YES, JULIE. I PROMISE. I'LL WRITE ... AND I'LL KEEP YOU IN MY HEART. UNTIL I SEE YOU AGAIN.

OH, ROBERTO ... I CAN'T BEAR TO LEAVE YOU!

Beth thought I was crazy, of course.

YOU MIGHT AS WELL FORGET HIM, NOW THAT WE'RE BACK HOME, JULIE. I'D A GOOD TIME WITH JUAN, TOO, BUT THAT'S ALL IT WAS. THEY'VE PROBABLY FORGOTTEN ALL ABOUT US NOW.

NO ... IT—IT WAS DIFFERENT FOR ME AND ROBERTO. I KNOW IT WAS!

Even my mum agreed with Beth.

YOU'RE NOT WRITING ANOTHER LETTER TO THAT BOY IN SPAIN, ARE YOU, JULIE?

YES, MUM. WE PROMISED WE'D WRITE TO EACH OTHER EVERY WEEK.

BUT NOBODY EVER KEEPS THOSE SORT OF PROMISES, LOVE. YOU'D BE BETTER TO FORGET HIM AND FIND SOME NICE LOCAL LAD.

OH, MUM, YOU DON'T UNDERSTAND ...

DEAR ROBERTO ... I WENT TO THE DISCO LAST NIGHT, BUT I CAME HOME AFTER HALF AN HOUR. I'M NOT INTERESTED IN CHATTING UP BOYS WITH BETH ANY MORE, BECAUSE ALL I CAN THINK OF IS YOU ...

And every week there was a letter for me from Spain ...

HE SAYS HE MISSES ME AND HE WISHES HE COULD SEE ME AGAIN. OH, ROBERTO, IF ONLY IT WAS POSSIBLE!

21

CUSHY NUMBERS!

These three great fun cushions will really brighten up your room. Exclusively designed for Patches by Alan Dart, you won't be able to resist them!

Our model is wearing a jacket and knickerbockers by Zed, tights by Mary Quant and leather pumps by Sacha.
Her bangle is from Adrien Mann.

pattern details on page 58.

22

A VIEW OF A ROOM

Fed up with your bedroom? Patches reader, Anne-Marie, wanted a new look for hers, so Patches decided to lend a helping hand and give you a few tips along the way! Here's how it looked when we saw it — now, turn the page and be amazed at what you can do with a bedroom like this . . .

ANNE-MARIE'S room is small with a tiny window, so we felt it just needed lots of white and primary colours to brighten it up. Luckily, her bed headboard and chest of drawers are white and will go with just about everything.

First of all, we stripped the old wallpaper and replaced it with two of Mayfair's New Wave wallpapers. They're both white with a graph pattern in red, blue, green and yellow and they transformed the room instantly. All the woodwork was painted blue to match the wallpaper. Then, to make sure we didn't lose any of the available light, we put up a white Pleatex blind. This is made of strong, washable paper and is very easy to assemble. The duvet cover and pillowcases are from Habitat and help to give the room a light, airy feeling.

To add a bit of colour, we used a table lamp with a red base, a mirror with a red frame and a red vegetable rack which is great for storing school work or papers. We made two cushions from the New Wave fabric and used a piece to cover the chest of drawers. The Palaset cube is the perfect size to hold all Anne-Marie's bits and pieces, and the two white rugs add the finishing touch!

Anne-Marie was delighted with the result. "I can't believe it's the same room," she said. "I can't wait to show my friends!"

WHAT WE USED

Mayfair New Wave Washable Wallpaper, left hand wall: New Fangled (BA 945); £3.75 per roll. Other walls: Quatro (BA 900); £3.75 per roll. Matching cotton fabric (PG 900); £3.75 per metre. Available from major department stores and D-I-Y stores. Winfield Gloss Paint in Blue Velvet, ½ litre tin, approx. 95p from Woolworths. White Pleatex blind from Habitat (catalogue No. N699136), ours had a 4 ft. drop and was 3 ft. 4 in. wide and cost £14.52. Prices vary according to size, other colours available. Table lamp from Habitat (catalogue No. N627011); £4.95. Crayon mirror with red plastic frame from Habitat (catalogue No. N613207); £3.75. Red vegetable rack by Habitat (catalogue No. N397725); £5.45. Duvet cover from Habitat (single size, catalogue No. N620513); £13.95. Pillowcases (catalogue No. N620823); £2.20 each. Palaset cube from Habitat with one shelf and door (catalogue No. F922501); £19.50. White rugs from Marks & Spencer; £7.99 each.

JOBS FOR THE GIRLS!

Jobs are hard to come by these days — and dream jobs even harder. But with a mixture of luck, self-confidence and an over-riding will to succeed, you can have a job you'll love!

FANCY your chances as a model, dancer, athlete . . .?

We know that finding a job at all these days is practically impossible, so making a career of something you really like doing, is a bit like trying to find the pot of gold at the end of the rainbow . . . a lovely dream which doesn't really exist. But . . . it can be done. You *can* have an interesting, rewarding career in a job you like and enjoy — if you've got enough determination.

We spoke to three young people who are all making names for themselves in varied jobs. Here's what they've got to say about their chosen careers.

SMILE, PLEASE!

MARY WATKINS is 18 and comes from Brighton. You may have seen her on the fashion pages of Patches, modelling for us. We asked Mary how she got started in the tough, competitive world of fashion modelling and she told us:

"I happened to bump into a friend whom I'd been at school with, and he asked if I'd be interested in being a sort of guinea-pig-cum-model at a hair show he was involved with. I said yes, and it just so happened that a famous hairdresser, Trevor Sorbie, was at the show. He asked me if I'd like to be a house model for him and of course I was delighted to be asked and said yes, please!

"That part was sheer luck! My second stroke of luck came after I'd done a few small modelling assignments. I was advised to go along to the modelling agency I'm with now — Askews — and show them the photographs I had. They then took me on as part of their team."

We asked Mary what she'd done before she struck lucky in the modelling business.

"Well, I worked for 10 months as a receptionist, though I didn't really want that type of job at all. But I simply couldn't find anything else. I really dreaded being stuck behind a desk for the rest of my life, though, so I finally left. I then thought perhaps I'd go to college and do a TOPS course. I'm quite interested in cooking so I was just investigating the possibility of doing a cookery course when I met that old school friend. I can't say I'm sorry I missed out on the course, because I'm really enjoying modelling at the moment, but I know a model's life is usually pretty short, in terms of her job, so maybe one day I'll go back to the cookery thing if it's not too late."

Any advice for potential models, we asked.

"Yes — be determined. Lots of people and situations can combine to make you feel as if you're getting nowhere fast, but if you stick to your guns and — most important — believe you've got what it takes, you'll get there in the end."

RUN RUN RUN!

At just 16, *LINSEY MACDONALD from Dunfermline in Fife, Scotland, was the toast of Great Britain when she and her team mates took the bronze medal for the 4 x 400 metres relay in the 1980 Olympics in Moscow. Linsey was the youngest-ever British athlete to compete in the Olympics, so her terrific performance was a double triumph for her.*

Linsey, who's now eighteen, was in the midst of studies for her final exams before leaving school when we spoke to her.

She started running when she was 11 and quickly gained medals in all the age group competitions she entered. She went on to win the Scottish Championship Intermediate 100 and 200 metres in June 1979 and also, in July of that year, she set a new British record for the 400 metres and was British Schools Champion in 100 and 400 metres. In honour of her achievements, Linsey was named Sportswoman of the year in 1980. All this is in addition to her school work, which is very important to her and which she obviously hasn't neglected, despite a punishing training programme. (Linsey has 4 Highers and 8 "O" levels to her credit, and when we talked, she was still trying to decide on which subject to aim for when she goes to university as she plans to.)

"I had almost decided on medicine as a career but I'm not absolutely certain yet." One thing she *was* sure of, though, was that whichever university she did eventually opt for, it would have to have first class training facilities so that she can continue running.

So, although running isn't a career as such — Linsey adheres strictly to the rules set down by the Scottish Amateur Athletics Association in order to preserve her amateur status — it certainly takes up a hefty slice of her life.

Linsey told us a typical week in her life means school each weekday, home at four to do an hour of homework, and then she has some tea and goes out at 6 for 2-3 hours training at her local club's track. Then it's back home to watch some TV and she's usually in bed by 10.30.

On a Friday, she occasionally has time for another hobby — disco-dancing; then at weekends it's more training. Linsey's coach, Tommy Bryce, has some rather unusual train-

ing methods: "Sometimes I run with a tyre dragging behind me attached to a rope round my waist; other times I've run in miners' pit boots — I don't mind really — when I put my spikes back on, it feels like I'm floating on air!"

Naturally, Linsey's sights are set on the 1984 Olympics in Los Angeles but there will be a few big events leading up to that — as well as numerous small events she's asked to attend now, such as opening fêtes and speaking at charity fund-raising efforts. Linsey has even had a street named after her in her home town — Linsey Macdonald Court. Not bad for a wee Scottish lass who's only 5 ft. 3¼ in. and weighs in at seven stones!

If Linsey does settle for medicine as her chosen career, we may one day see the unusual sight of a petite doctor in running spikes and shorts doing the daily rounds with lightning speed!

FACING UP TO IT

The next person we spoke to took us back to the glamorous world of models and glossy magazines. At 19, DEBORAH BUN is one of a growing band of experts whose job it is to make the models in the magazines look so beautiful we'll all want to copy them!

She's a professional make-up artist who, in fact, shares a flat with our model, Mary Watkins. Deborah told us that her entry into the business was also due partly to luck, in the first instance.

A friend of hers who is a designer and knew she was interested in make-up, asked if she'd like to help with a show he was putting on and, naturally, Deborah jumped at the chance!

This led to other shows and Deborah gradually built up some contacts whom she kept in touch with, whilst she was on the lookout for all the work she could get.

When we asked about the tools of the trade, Deborah told us: "I started off with just the things I had myself and lots of ideas! Gradually, I built up my kit and I've now got every different colour of eye shadow, blusher, foundation and lipstick you could think of. I carry them all round in a plastic tool box."

Deborah has been doing the job now for about a year and a half and mostly works for magazines and advertising companies, making up models for the camera. She is a freelance make-up artist, which means that although she is on the Askew model agency team who send her along to fashion and beauty sessions if the magazine requests a make-up artist. She also does other kinds of work — for fashion shows, videos, etc.

When we spoke to her, Deborah was very excited about a new commission she was going to be working on: "I've been asked to do the make-up for a West End stage play and I'm really looking forward to it as it will be totally different to making up girls for a camera."

For the future, she says:

"I'd really like to get into TV work but the BBC don't employ make-up artists until they're 21, so I'll have to wait a while yet!"

The Princess And The Dragon

LIGHT streaked across the sky, throwing the bleak castle into stark relief. Dark and forbidding, it glowered at anyone foolish enough to look towards it. But in the topmost window of the topmost tower blinked one glimmer of light — for this was Princess Kyla's prison.

Years ago, Wizard Bogmarrow had invaded the kingdom of Fairhaven and kidnapped King Frankle's daughter, Kyla. The wizard hated the King and was determined to defeat him in any possible way. He knew the King adored his only child and that kidnapping was the perfect method of attack.

However, when the Princess was locked up in the castle, Wizard Bogmarrow was engaged in a terrible conflict with a neighbouring wizard and was slain. Meanwhile, the King, grief-stricken at the loss of his daughter, died of a broken heart. The Princess remained imprisoned and seemingly forgotten.

A fearsome dragon slept under the hill that the castle stood on. He was a livid green, with frightful scales that soared up into the air. One baleful, scarlet eye remained open constantly, even in sleep — a terrifying jailor indeed. His skin was so sensitive that he could feel the slightest pressure of a footfall on the hill. Princes and Knights, hearing of Kyla's plight had ridden out to save her — but the dragon slept on their bones now and shrieked with evil laughter as he felt each new horse approach.

Up in her prison turret, Kyla wept each day, totally in despair. Her food was pushed through a crack beneath the door by an old hag who knew nothing of the Wizard's death. Besides, she was under a spell herself and couldn't speak — why have any sympathy for Kyla?

Each day, the Princess gazed out of the window, praying for release, while the dragon, as if sensing her wish, shook his scaley wings and howled and hissed in the night.

One day, a terrible storm was raging over the land and the whole castle trembled in its foundations. A fierce wind whipped and whistled for hours. Kyla was sitting in her room shivering with cold when a large leaf was suddenly blown in through the side of the tiny window. She ran to the window at once and took up the leaf. There was a tiny pencil stub hidden away, just in case. Taking this, Kyla wrote a rather shaky message on the leaf and then flung it out through the crack, on to the wind again. And then, she sat down to wait . . .

MANY leagues away, a young farm worker was labouring in the fields. He was tall and handsome and a great help to his father. He was bent double, toiling against the wind when a large, wet leaf slapped into his face! Brimen peeled it from his eye only to see the shaky message from Princess Kyla. Now Brimen was no prince of royal blood but he couldn't resist this cry from a princess and set off at once to see his grandfather, Old Garleen.

Garleen was wise and knowing and told

A special Patches fairy story by Mary Martin

Brimen everything he knew about Princess Kyla. He described the evil dragon until Brimen was shaking.

"This dragon sleeps with one eye open and can sense any movement, even at the very edge of the hill. No-one has ever been successful in the mission because the secret of the dragon's eye is known to few people. Those that have the knowledge mention it rarely — for in the wrong hands it could create utter chaos!

"I studied for many years with a master magician and, as he lay dying he passed the secret on to me, because he had no son. I hoped I would never need to utter those words to anyone, but you must do as you think best. The potion has to be thrown directly into the dragon's eye. But first you must think of a way to reach the castle without the dragon sensing you — but that is for you to solve . . ."

Brimen had a heavy heart as he left his grandfather with the list of ingredients for the magic potion. The task seemed impossible, but he couldn't desert the Princess! He spent long nights pondering the problem, until one day the solution leapt into his mind! He rose quickly and made his way into the fields. A long time ago, Brimen had rescued the son of the Mole King from a cruel and deadly trap and the Mole King had pledged allegiance ever since.

Brimen called on the King now and explained his problem. Together they

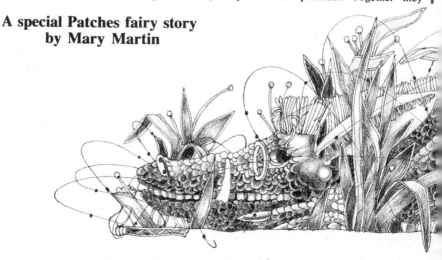

worked out a plan and Brimen thanked him, promising to call on him again soon, and set off to gather the ingredients for the potion.

He hoped the Princess hadn't given up hope as he set off into the mountains, for he knew his task would be long.

There were eight ingredients in all; every one involving tremendous difficulties. Brimen knew his courage and strength would be tested to the utmost but he thrust his head high and marched on into the night.

He found a tiny wooden lodge that would be his home for the next few months and immediately set to work. Just looking at the list made him tremble with fear:

Two seeds from the pod of the Cardyn plant; one claw from the Kasleen — a leathery, shrieking bird that chilled every-one to the bone with its evil cry; a single hair plucked from the head of Ogren — an old hag who lived alone in a cave, mutter-ing spells through the night; three drops of poison from the skin of the mottled brown toad with deadly, cold eyes; the cast-off skin of a vicious snake that guarded all its skins with jealousy and slowly throttled its victims to death; a phial of water from the dripping, foul pool by a certain, dead oak-if anyone touched or drank this water their blood ran cold and thick at once; one blade of grass from the razor-sharp field of rushes that closed round and pierced to the core any invader to their field; and, lastly, an egg from the nest of the Beazon — a particularly repulsive, nasty reptile that crawled round on its belly, drooling and shedding venom constantly and only leaving its nest once a year.

Fearful adventures followed as Brimen was beset by fantastic creatures, but his courage never failed him and as the months passed, so his collection grew.

HOWEVER, there was one ingredient that seemed to haunt him. "Take two seeds from the pod of the Cardyn plant." It sounded an easy enough task, but didn't add that the Cardyn plant was a flesh-eater! It had long, sinewy tentacles which could smell anything living. When it located any prey, these arms would shoot out like lightning and its vice-like grip could not be broken. Brimen watched

countless animals come to grief at the hands of this monster but he could do nothing.

To complicate matters even more, the pod was right in the very heart of the plant, guarded with utmost care by the tentacles. For once, Brimen's courage started to fail him — he had never felt so alone.

One day, Brimen was watching the plant in despair, racking his brains for a solution. Then, suddenly, his attention was caught by a chimp swinging along the vines high above. The chimp was intent on mischief and generally enjoying himself, when its eye was caught by a large, juicy borrog fruit — delicious, a great favourite with chimps, but with a very tough skin. The chimp leapt towards the fruit, grabbed it, knocked it from the branch, but couldn't catch it. The borrog started to spin and dropped towards the earth — landing smack in the middle of the Cardyn plant and breaking the pod from the heart!

Brimen could not believe his luck as the pod rolled towards him and slowly came to a halt at his feet. His astonishment was complete, but he was overcome with laughter at the outcome of the matter! Then, hastily picking up the pod, he waved and shouted his thanks to the chimp, who was far too busy mourning the fate of his borrog to be in the slightest bit interested, and then Brimen went on his way.

So, finally, one grey morning Brimen stumbled from the hills with the last ingredient wrapped safely in his cloak. But a further delay followed as Brimen watched for the full moon. He had little sleep these days — his ingredients were far too precious to risk losing.

At last, the moon rose full and heavy, casting a milky light over the land. Brimen placed each ingredient on the ground in front of the cauldron he'd borrowed from his grandfather. His hands shook slightly but he began his task. Each item was dropped with great care into the pot — and he read the words of the spell over each new addition. The words frightened him, but the thought of Princess Kyla kept him strong. As the moon began to wane, the final ingredient was added and the evil potion steamed and winked from the pot — ready to cancel out the dragon's eye.

Brimen prepared himself at last. He bade

Continued on page 30

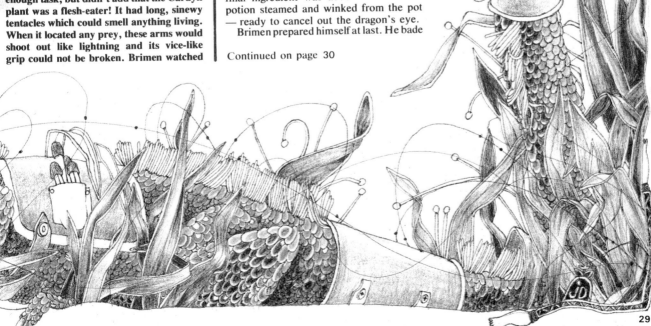

29

farewell to his father and grandfather, and with their calls ringing in his ears he set off to the castle. On his way he dropped in to see the Mole King and to arrange an agreed signal for the King's help.

ON he walked, league after league — the potion hissing and bubbling as he neared the dragon's home. And then, as the dawn approached one day, Brimen saw the castle silhouetted against the sky, with the hill dominating the scene.

He walked slowly towards this hill — very gently he went until he was at the foot of the hill. Then he began to tap on the ground with two sticks in a very gentle, strange rhythm. Lo and behold, thousands of moles appeared, burrowing up from every imaginable place! They scurried and burrowed up the hill making it tremble and move.

The dragon in his lair was dumbfounded. The tremors were so great that terrible confusion set in and he didn't know what was travelling up the hill. Meanwhile, Brimen seized advantage of the situation, and leapt towards the dragon. The potion was now smoking and bubbling furiously.

Brimen dashed into the lair, scattering bones, and flung the potion at the dragon's eye. There was an ear-splitting shriek and the ground trembled and shook. Brimen was thrown to the ground and covered his head with his hands.

Gradually, the ground grew still and Brimen looked up. The dragon was sprawled in his corner, both eyes closed and no danger to anyone ever again. Brimen jumped to his feet, ran to thank the moles and then entered the castle.

Cobwebs and dust coated everything in sight and Brimen ran from room to room. Finally, he saw a tiny corridor and a staircase. Up and up he went, until he arrived at a great door. Through a minute peep-hole he spied Princess Kyla trembling in the corner at the awful rumblings from the dragon's lair.

With the dragon dead, the spells were broken and Brimen threw open the door . . . It was love at first sight, obviously, and Brimen carried the Princess downstairs.

What a sight it was as Brimen and Kyla passed through the land with thousands of moles as their guard of honour!

There was rejoicing throughout the land at the death of the wicked dragon. The wedding of Princess Kyla and Brimen was one of the most splendid occasions ever seen.

And, of course, they lived happily ever after . . .

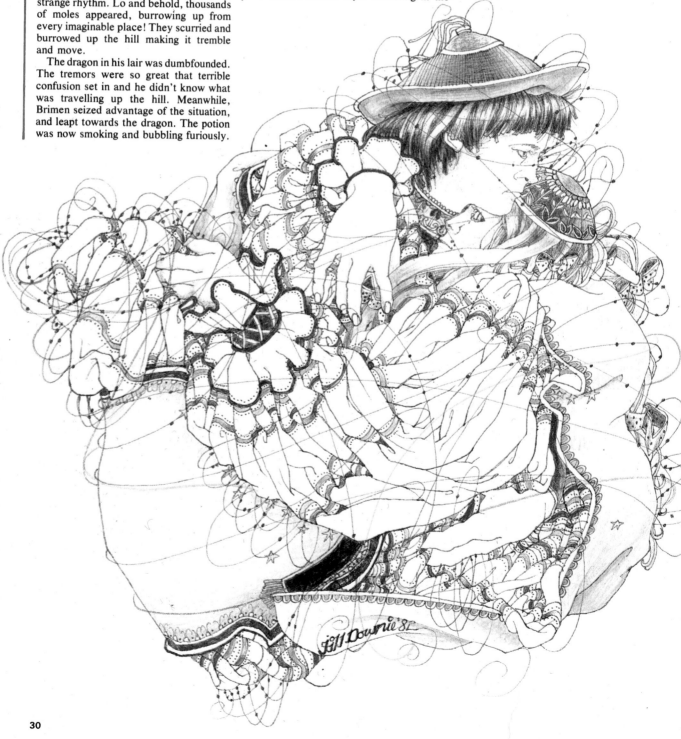

Fun On A Shoestring!

Feeling in a rut and cleaned out of cash? Well, cheer up! You don't have to be a millionaire to get a few giggles out of life. In fact, there are a thousand and one fun things you can do that cost next to nothing and are anything but boring. Interested? Then read on . . .

SUPER SWAPS

There's nothing better than a party for cheering you up, so how about you and your mates getting together and organising The Incredibly Awful Swap-Shop?

Everybody's got something awful lurking at the back of their wardrobe or the bottom of their drawer that they'd dearly like to get rid of.

For instance, Great Uncle Fred's birthday present to you last year of the Complete Works of Algernon Higgenbottom, which has been helping prop up the wobbly leg of your bedside table for the last twelve months, could just be somebody else's idea of Heaven!

OK, so maybe you'll swap it for something as useless, such as a pink woolly rabbit, and your bedside table'll collapse — but at least you'll get a laugh or two. And that's the best thing we know for beating the blues!

On a more serious level, a Swap-Shop can be a useful source of new clothes. You may be fed up with that disco outfit you bought, not so long ago, but if your best friend has had her eye on it, there's no reason why you shouldn't swap it for something of hers that you fancy, is there?

GET OUT YOUR PEN!

But if you don't fancy that, you could always go in for competitions, instead. Lots of magazines run these, and so do manufacturers who're promoting special products.

Normally, the only qualifications you need to enter are your imagination and the price of a stamp! And who knows? It'll not only keep you occupied for half an hour, but you could actually get lucky and win a Giant Size Paper Robot or a year's supply of Crunchy Catfood. (If you haven't got a cat, either get one — which'll also stop you being bored — or flog the Crunchy stuff to someone who has and make yourself a tidy little profit!)

Feeling lonely as well as bored? Find yourself a penfriend! Keep an eye on ''Paper Mates'' in Patches and see if anybody crops up there you fancy writing to. Alternatively, drop us a line and enter **yourself** as a prospective Paper Mate — then sit back and wait for the letters to flood in!

WHAT'S COOKING?

But what if you're not into writing? Well, you could take up cooking instead.

At a very small cost you could invest in ''The Beginner's Cook Book'' by Betty Falk (Penguin Paperbacks) and it'll tell you, in very simple language — with illustrations — how to make a risotto, a sausage roll and a cheese straw.

Not quite you, you're thinking? Hang on a second! If your cheese straws go down a treat you could always package 'em up and sell 'em off at the next jumble sale or Swap-Shop, couldn't you? That way, not only do you stop being bored — you make money as well! Of course, if you eat them all as soon as you make them, you'll not only get bored again — as well as penniless — you'll get **fat**, too.

Well, we never said any of this was going to be easy, did we?

OUT AND ABOUT

So you're not the domestic type, huh? Well, leave the pots 'n' pans behind and sample the endless delights of the Great Outdoors! For a start, do a bit of walking.

There are lots of walks open to the public all over the countryside now, and ''Spurbooks Footpath Guides,'' which you should be able to get hold of in your local library, could lead you on all sorts of weird and wonderful rambles! Take a friend or two for company, and you'll enjoy yourself even more.

HOW TO BEAT THE BLUES

But how else can you beat boredom without costing yourself a fortune? Here's a list of personal favourites compiled by the Patches team — some daft, some practical, but all designed to beat the boredom blues . . .

1. Get all your mates to contribute 50p, con Dad into buying a large tin of paint, then throw a re-decorating-your-own-room party.

2. Go on a charity walk/run/jog/swim. At least you'll be fit.

3. Take a dog for a walk. If you like dogs, this can be fun and a way of meeting other people who like dogs — that boy down the street, f'r instance . . .

4. Stargaze. Finding out where Ursae Minoris and Canum Venaticorum is, can actually be fantastically exciting if you've got someone nice to keep you company!

5. Take up gardening. It can be very relaxing, sitting waiting for a seed to sprout!

6. Write the story of your life so far. You might think it's boring, but other folk might find it amazingly intriguing! You never know, it could be a best-seller!

7. Have a 60's evening with all your mates. Get them to turn up in 60's gear and bring with them all the 60's records their parents still have. You won't be bored and we guarantee you'll be hysterical with laughter.

8. Take up jogging!

So there you are! Masses of ways to help you get out of a boring rut! Why not add some of your own ideas to our list — you'll be so busy thinking up crazy schemes, the last thing you'll have time to do is feel bored!

We got together a few bits and pieces of accessories – and the results were quite hair raising! It's not a case of hair today, gone tomorrow with these hairstyles – they'll look good any time, any place – and they'll always be in the news!

3. Polka dots, pearls — and beaded sewing trimmings help make this misty blue romantic look! The polka dots are a haircomb and the trimmings are simply wound round Fiona's bunch of curls.

1. This sparkling black net scarf wound bandeau fashion round Ellen's ruffled hair gives her an exotic Eastern air. We clipped the golden thread-bound coin grip on to the actual scarf to hold it in place on the hair.

5. Tracy's a real bow belle with this hairband! And the silky green bow is just large and floppy enough for her delicate features.

4. Hairbands don't have to sit in one place — try one this way! The dainty golden butterfly comb adds sparkle to Fiona's golden locks.

6. Multi-coloured thread-bound hairgrips, a plait and a tiny gingham hair-tier give Tracy a completely different look here.

2. The red tier and red, black and gold hairband make this high ponytail fashionable fun!

Hair accessories and jewellery from selections at Boots, Salisbury's, Top Shop and Debenhams. Clothes from Top Shop and Debenhams.

1,000,00 YEARS BP

BEFORE PATCHES

EUREKA THE WHEEL

A PATCHES PREHISTORIC PHOTO STORY

There was really only one thing wrong with being a girl in prehistoric times—the boys!

GRUNT-GRUNT... SNORT...SNUFFLE-UFFLE...GRUNT-URP...

OH, TROG, YOU SAY THE SWEETEST THINGS! IF ONLY I COULD UNDERSTAND THEM!

Oona and Trog were members of the stick-people tribe...

STICK-PEOPLE AM GREAT TRIBE. WORSHIP TREES! AS STRONG AS TREES! AS TALL AS TREES! AS TOUGH AS TREES!

HMM—AND, UNFORTUNATELY, AS THICK AS THEM, TOO!

This is Uggi...

THERE'S OONA! SHE'S BEAUTIFUL! I REALLY... I MEAN I'M...I MEAN SHE MAKES ME FEEL SO...

IT'S REALLY TOUGH NOT HAVING A WORD FOR LOVE IN OUR LANGUAGE! I CAN'T DESCRIBE HOW...I... HOW MUCH I...

C

34

BUT THOSE ARE HIS GOOD POINTS! WHAT IS IT YOU DON'T LIKE ABOUT HIM?

HE REMINDS ME OF A PIECE OF WOOD SINKING IN A SMELLY, SWAMPY, FILTHY BOG!

OK, SO HE'S A STICK-IN-THE-MUD! BUT YOU'LL JUST HAVE TO GET USED TO THAT AND—

NO! I'M THROUGH WITH TROG! I'M GOING TO CHOOSE MY OWN BOY!

Of course, that could mean only one thing . . .

OUT THEN! YOU ARE BANISHED FROM OUR TRIBE! GO, AND NEVER DARKEN OUR TREEBARK AGAIN.

GOOD RIDDANCE! I DON'T CARE!

BUT I DO CARE. I DON'T THINK UGGI'S EVER NOTICED ME, SO I'M DOOMED TO WANDER FOREVER IN THE WILDERNESS ALONE!

OF COURSE, IT COULD BE WORSE. TROG COULD HAVE COME WITH ME. OH, WELL . . . HERE GOES . . .

But before she got very far . . .

OONA! WH- WHAT ARE YOU DOING HERE?

OH, I'VE BEEN BANISHED FROM MY TRIBE. I THOUGHT I'D NIP OUT AND WANDER IN THE WASTE-LAND FOR A DOZEN YEARS OR SO . . .

BUT THE WILDERNESS IS FULL OF ANIMALS! DINOSAURS, BIG CATS, SNAKES, SPIDERS . . . LOOK!

" Brontosaurus . . . Tyrannosaurus . . . Pterodactyls . . . Giant Lizards . . . "

IF YOU'RE TRYING TO CHEER ME UP YOU'RE NOT DOING TOO GOOD A JOB! ARE THOSE ANIMALS WILD?

WILD? THEY'RE ABSOLUTELY FURIOUS! WOULDN'T YOU BE IF ALL YOU HAD TO LOOK FORWARD TO WAS EXTINCTION?

37

PATCHES AMAZING POP FACTS!

Astound your friends with your knowledge of silly but fascinating information! Patches gives you lots and lots of useless pop information at your fingertips!

*Gerry and the Pacemakers' first three hit records reached No. 1.

*The Bay City Rollers got their name by placing a pin in a map.

*Deep Purple played The Rainbow in 1972 and three people were carried out unconscious because the noise level reached 117 decibels — which is the equivalent of standing fifty metres from a jumbo jet as it takes off!

*Dave Wakeling of The Beat was a fireman, bingo caller, lifeguard, brickie and solar panel maker amongst other things.

*"This Ole House" — a hit for Shakin' Stevens — was written by Stuart Hamblem on a paper bag after he found the body of a man in a hut twenty miles from the nearest road.

*Debbie Harry's favourite groups are The Runaways, Ramones, Talking Heads, Devo and Sex Pistols.

*"Yesterday" — written by Paul McCartney and John Lennon — has been recorded nearly 1200 times.

*Toyah's favourite food is octopus.

Alan's Top Ten.
1. American Pie – Don McLean.
2. Another Piece of Meat – Scorpions.
3. Banana Rock – The Wombles.
4. Black Pudding Bertha – The Goodies.
5. Breakfast In America – Supertramp.
6. Cut The Cake – Average White Band.
7. Green Onions – Booker T and the MGs.
8. Life Is A Minestrone – 10cc.
9. Toast – The Streetband.
10. Fattie Bum Bum – Carl Malcolm.

*Mike Nolan of Buck's Fizz is NOT related to the Nolan Sisters.

*When the original Human League split up, Phil Oakey and Adrian Wright retained the name by giving Ian Marsh and Martyn Ware (now Heaven 17) one per cent of the royalties on "Dare" which was a huge seller. It's estimated that Marsh and Ware have netted over £20,000 for an LP which they had nothing to do with!

*Elvis Presley spent 1077 weeks in the charts.

*It took Johnny Mathis 18 years 216 days from his first chart hit to get to number one.

*The Beatles had eleven No. 1 hits in a row.

*It took David Bowie's "Space Oddity" 6 years 63 days to reach No. 1 from the date of its release.

*UB40 got their name from a form which you fill in when you claim dole money.

*If you've got a copy of "Liza Jane" by Davey Jones and the King Bees, don't throw it out, it's worth about one hundred pounds now. Why? Davey Jones is now David Bowie!

*"River Deep Mountain High" sung by Ike and Tina Turner and produced by Phil Spector in 1966, cost 22,000 dollars to make — an amazing amount of money for those days. As if that wasn't enough, it flopped in America.

The Ed's Top Ten.
1. *I Don't Like Mondays – Boomtown Rats.*
2. *Hooray Hooray It's A Holi-Holiday – Boney M.*
3. *I Believe In Father Christmas – Greg Lake.*
4. *I Talk To The Trees – Clint Eastwood.*
5. *I'm A Clown – David Cassidy.*
6. *I Might Be Lying – Eddie And The Hot Rods.*
7. *I'm The Leader Of The Gang – Gary Glitter.*
8. *Accidents Will Happen – Elvis Costello.*
9. *No More Mr Nice Guy – Alice Cooper.*
10. *You Won't Find Another Fool Like Me – New Seekers.*

Here are some mad song titles from the Eurovision Song Contest:
Boum bada Boum — Monaco '67.
Boom Bang-A-Bang — UK '69.
Oj Oj Oj — Norway '69.
Ding Ding Dong — Holland '75.
Pump Pump — Finland '76.
Boom Boom Boomerang — Austria '77.
A-B-Ni-Bi — Israel '78.

Patches People Top Ten Hated Records:
1. Birdie Song — The Tweets.
2. Shaddup You Face — Joe Dolce.
3. There's No-One Quite Like Grandma — St Winifred's School Choir.
4. Anything by Starsound.
5. Y Viva Espagna — Sylvia.
6. Shifting Whispering Sands — Eammon Andrews.
7. Anything by Showaddywaddy.
8. Matchstick Men — Brian and Michael.
9. Oh Julie — Shakin' Stevens.
10. Mull of Kintyre — Wings.

EVER wanted to be swept off your feet by Adam Ant? To take another pot-shot (one that works this time!) at J.R.? To spend a day lying on a beach in the South Seas listening to the surf and talking to Tarzan?

Well, we've got news for you! Now you *can!* All you have to do is dream!

"Huh!" we hear you sneer. "Now pull the other leg! I'm always having dreams, but they're about that spotty guy at Number 39, or Mum's rubber plant, and I never remember 'em properly anyway!"

Correct!

But what you're doing is simply dreaming any old dream that comes into your head. You're not having what is called *a lucid dream.*

Lucid dreams are funny things which usually only happen rarely, but they're an experience to remember!

In a lucid dream, the dreamer actually *knows* she's dreaming!

It sounds crazy, but it works something like this. The dreamer

goes to sleep. After an interval, she starts dreaming. But at this point the dreamer splits herself in two (not literally, of course!).

One part of her is dreaming about lying on that beach in the South Seas. The *other* part is lying in bed actually *watching* the dream as it happens, much the same way you sit in front of the telly and watch "Coronation Street"!

The best thing about a lucid dream is that the *dreamer* can actually control what's happening! Instead of being swept along the way you are in a normal dream, you can actually get up and walk

into your mental television set.

You can have an argument with Hilda Ogden, flirt with Brian Tilsley, or empty a pint of bitter over Annie Walker's head! It's entirely up to you and how you feel, because *you* are making it all happen! It was your brain that made all this up in the first place!

Everyone has dreams — some good, some bad, some downright frightening.

Solve All Your Problems!

Lucid dreams are very handy when it comes to dealing with problems.

Think of it this way. Your brain is actually in two parts, and the parts are bridged by a sort of telegraph system of nerves.

In a right-handed person, the left part of the brain deals with reason and words and memory, while the right side deals with

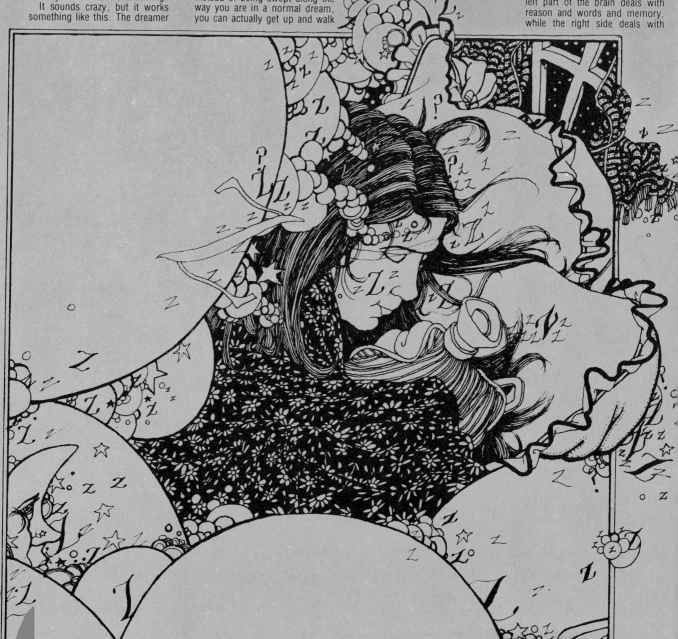

Dreams

If you'd like to find out what your dreams mean — and even how to control them — just read on!

patterns and designs. All that happens when you dream is that a message is passed from one side of the brain to the other. But you and your brain created that "message" in the first place, so you can control the "message" in any way you want to!

F'r example, you may have a dream when you're standing in the middle of a room full of strangers. They're all beautifully dressed, perfectly friendly and chatting away to you — but *you're* in your birthday suit!

Not only is this a *problem* — it's an embarrassing problem!

However, your *mind* created that problem, therefore your mind actually knows the reason *why* it created it! Something, in other words, is bugging your sub-conscious.

In a lucid dream, unlike an ordinary one, you can actually *approach* the problem. You can ask the other people why they're all dressed and you're not. They'll give you the answers, and when you wake up the following morning you may very well discover that all that worrying you were doing about what to wear for a special date has disappeared because — for example — someone in your dream perhaps told you that it isn't what a person *wears* that counts, it's what a person *is*!

There's a tribe of Indians who actually run their entire every-day lives based on their "dreaming" lives. And they have three simple dream rules.

1. **Don't run away from anything in your dreams. Overcome the dangers.**
2. **Go *towards* pleasant experiences.** If you're in the middle of a muddy field and there's a beautiful field full of daffodils and sunlight on the other side of a river — find a way to cross the river. (You can do it! It's your dream! There are no holds barred! You can suddenly develop wings and fly if you like. Nobody's going to tell you not to!)
3. **Always make sure your dreams end *positively*.** If you've been going through a lucid dream where you were having a stand-up row with your dad, don't just let it end with him slam-

ming out of the room and having the final word. Get *your* say in, too!

In your dream world, if you can meet any dangers — from raging lions to nasty creepy-crawlies — head on and find a way of dealing with them, there's a fair chance you'll be able to do that in real life too.

The same thing goes for angry dreams, or sad dreams, or despairing dreams, because the very simple link between a dream-at-night and the real-world-in-the-morning is — emotion. What you *see* in your dreams may not in any way be real. But what you *feel* is!

How To Have A Lucid Dream

Right — having more or less explained what lucid dreams are, all you've got to do now is learn how to do it!

For a start, you must wake yourself up once you've had a dream. Most people do actually wake for a fraction of a second after dreaming, but they go straight back to sleep again and don't realise they've been awake.

So, there you are in bed. *Before* you go to sleep at all, just mutter to yourself three or four times, "I'm going to wake up after a dream." Your mind should do the rest for you, just because you've given it a mental note!

When you *do* wake up, start remembering the dream. Keep a pencil and notepad beside the bed and jot down all the things you dreamed about.

Then, for about fifteen minutes, keep yourself fully awake. Get up and make a cup of tea. Feed the cat. Talk to the moon. Read a book. Brush your teeth — anything that makes you fully conscious.

Just before you go back to sleep get yourself fully relaxed — you can do this quite simply by concentrating on each part of your body in turn, starting with your toes and working slowly up to the top of your head. When you *are* relaxed, tell yourself that the next time you dream you're going to remember *what*

you dream.

Now, shut your eyes and *imagine* you're already asleep. See yourself snuggled down in bed clutching your hot-water bottle with the sheets pulled up to your chin. Once you've got that picture firmly in your mind's eye, *imagine* your eyelids have

started to flicker and that you're actually having the same dream you wrote about when you woke up the first time.

Go over it again, but at the same time be aware you're imagining you're lying in bed asleep! (Phew!)

Go through the whole process again several times until you've got a clear idea of what you *want* to happen. Don't worry if you find it difficult to wake up in the first place, or find it even more difficult not to go to sleep while you're *imagining* you're asleep. With time and practice you will be able to have these lucid dreams.

The Meaning Of Your Dreams

But, we hear you ask, what use is all this, really?

Well, apart from being a lot of fun — understanding your dreams really *can* help you solve problems.

F'r example, *all* dreams have general meanings which don't vary at all from person to person.

Dreaming that you're running means there are various things worrying you. If you dream you're running but eventually reach a particular place — then the dream is a good sign and means your worries'll soon be over.

In a *lucid* dream, if you're running and constantly coming up against obstacles or difficulties, or if people are chasing you, you can actually *stop*, take a clear look at what the obstacles are *and* ask the people just *why* they're chasing you!

Once you've recognised just what the things are that're standing in your way (and you will), and heard what the people have to say — you'll have a clearer idea of what your actual problem is. In the morning, when you're awake, you'll remember — and the chances are you'll be able to solve the problem!

Dreaming about receiving some kind of unexpected present always used to mean the opposite to what was actually happening. It was a sort of warning that you should think twice about whoever was giving you the present.

In a lucid dream, you don't have to think twice or worry.

All you've got to do is *ask* the person why they're giving you the present!

Dreaming about a cat is supposed to mean someone you trust is going to hurt you in some way.

But in *your* lucid dream, if you do happen to meet a cat, you can talk to it — and there's absolutely no reason why it shouldn't chat back to you! You're controlling the dream, after all, and your dream-cat can be made to speak English as clearly as you do. (Cats probably can speak English anyhow, they're just too superior to admit it!)

Lucid dreaming means you can make sense of your dreams *right at the moment you're having them*.

With ordinary dreams you've got to try to remember details when you wake up, and there's nearly always something — usually something important — that you just *can't* recall.

There's nothing more infuriating than wishing you could put your finger on the missing piece of the puzzle — and not being able to. It's like having an itch you can't scratch! But with lucid dreaming, this problem just doesn't arise.

So open up a whole new magical mystery world for yourself!

Let Adam Ant or Prince Andrew sweep you away to a fairy tale castle!

Be Debbie Harry for the evening!

Laze on the beach and listen to the surf!

Become all the things *you* want to become . . . .

Sweet dreams!

The 70's were the days of platform shoes, Bay City Rollers, smock tops and feather cuts, to name just a few fascinating crazes. Here, we've taken a quick look at 1970-75, just for a laugh. (Wonder what they'll be saying about us in ten years' time?!)

Back to the 70's

THE LOOKS

Eyebrows were pencil thin, often giving people a permanently surprised expression. False eyelashes were still popular. Hair was parted in the centre and long—until the Feather Cut swept the nation. Here, the hair was heavily layered all over leaving a long, wispy fringe at the back.

On July 5th and 6th, 1974, Jimmy Connors and Chris Evert won the Singles Championships at Wimbledon and announced their engagement.

Princess Anne married Captain Mark Phillips on November 14, 1973.

THE CLOTHES

Practically everyone in the country became four inches taller overnight! This amazing feat was due to platform shoes which were huge, heavy and clumsy. However, they did keep your feet warm (due to the fact that the ground was a long way away!) and they did wonders for shorties. Desert boots were really popular, too, and Jesus sandals were the summer favourites.

Britain's money went decimal in February '71 and we said goodbye to half crowns and shillings.

Trousers were baggy and flared, and either very long or halfway up calves. They were often high-waisted with up to eight buttons on the waistband. Mini skirts were worn with

middle parting

long spikey lashes

pencil thin eyebrows

pink lipstick

long straight hair

midi or maxi coats on top. Maxi dresses—especially pinafores—were very popular.

Jumpers were being worn for the first time, and practically everything could be bought in tartan, thanks to the Bay City Rollers.

Abba won the Eurovision Song Contest in '74 with "Waterloo"—their first British hit.

The craze for streaking (running naked through the streets!) started in America in early '74.
27th May, 1974, 35,000 fans thronged the White City Stadium in London to see David Cassidy.

Smock tops and dresses were great for anyone who had anything to hide, and no trouser suit was complete without a chain belt.

At the end of '73, there was an energy crisis due to a coal shortage. 50 m.p.h. speed limits were put on roads; street lighting was cut by half; there was restricted heating in shops and offices and everywhere suffered from frequent blackouts . . .

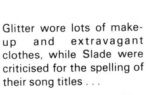

THE MUSIC

In the early '70's, popstars were really popstars. They played in the biggest venues possible and were always untouchable.

Suzi Quatro was just about the only female on the pop scene. Sweet, David Bowie and Gary

Glitter wore lots of make-up and extravagant clothes, while Slade were criticised for the spelling of their song titles . . .

Here are some No. 1 hits from '70 to '75:

Hot Love—T Rex
Maggie May—Rod Stewart
I'd Like To Teach The World To Sing—New Seekers
Puppy Love—Donny Osmond
Mama Weer All Crazee Now—Slade
Blockbuster—Sweet
See My Baby Jive—Wizzard
I'm The Leader Of The Gang—Gary Glitter
Tiger Feet—Mud
Devil Gate Drive—Suzi Quatro
Love Me For A Reason—Osmonds
Gonna Make You A Star—David Essex
Down Down—Status Quo
Bye Bye Baby—Bay City Rollers
I'm Not In Love—10cc
Bohemian Rhapsody—Queen

It's their world, too!

Just testing

ANIMALS are used for medical and cosmetic research.

Rabbits are used frequently because they can't cry. When a new kind of eye make-up, for example, is being created, small quantities of the substances used are put in the rabbits' eyes to check the reaction. As a rabbit can't "cry" it can't, obviously, wash away the foreign substance!

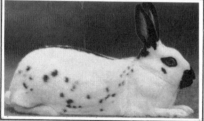

Skin irritation tests are carried out on *monkeys*. Their stomachs are shaved. Small dabs of various creams are applied to the shaved area, then covered in Elastoplast and left to see if any irritation *does* occur.

So what, you may think.

But how many rabbits wear eye make-up? And how many monkeys, in their natural surroundings, get themselves covered in cream and Elastoplast?

Is it all *really* necessary — just so we can look prettier or sexier?

The hunt is on

MANKIND has always used animals one way or another, and it has always hunted them. Sometimes there were good reasons for this. More recently, there haven't been.

Whales, for instance, have been around for about 30 million years — almost ten times as long as we have!

Before anybody discovered petroleum, whale blubber was a main source of cooking and heating oil. So whales were hunted. One species after another has been harpooned practically out of existence!

But they're *still* being hunted — despite the work done by various conservation societies. Yet modern chemical plants can produce all the products we get from whales more cheaply, more efficiently, and less dangerously!

Unfortunately, however, sheer human greed has got an awful lot to answer for!

A fur coat made from South American *ocelots* can cost as much as £20,000.

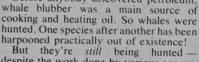

A rare orchid or an Amazonian *parrot* can fetch as much as £3000.

A *rhino* horn (which isn't truly a horn at all) is worth its weight in gold because people are convinced it has medicinal properties. *It hasn't.*

So what on earth is the point in carrying on with this absurd one-upmanship?

Food for thought

ANIMALS, right at the moment, are getting a very, very raw deal.

In America, *battery chickens* which are specially bred for everybody's Sunday lunch actually have their beaks cut off so they can't peck at each other. Why? Because if they damage another prospective lunch, the organisation breeding them loses a little bit of profit!

Most animals which are moved around as "food" are transported in the most appalling conditions. Live chickens are jammed into crates. *Calves* are wedged

side by side in dark containers. And they're often deprived of food and water on their sad journey from the farm to the slaughter-house.

In England, poaching is on the increase. But the days of the shifty little poacher in the cloth cap have disappeared. Now they come from towns in cars with false number plates. They use citizen's band radio and work in twos and threes.

They use cyanide gas to kill *fish*, and snares — nooses or stretched piano wire — to catch *deer*. *Pheasants* are blinded by light, then shot with a catapult or an air pistol. There have been reports of deer caught in traps and left for days until they literally starved to death.

But if all this sounds horrendous, what's happening with ordinary cats and dogs is even *worse*.

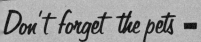

Every minute of every day, somewhere in the world, something is happening to the animal, bird and insect population. And in nine cases out of ten, people are responsible! Whether it's because of hunting and poaching, cruel methods of product testing, a desire for a fur coat or the destruction of habitat, or simply because too few people care, many animals are in danger of extinction.

The delicate balance of Nature is constantly being upset by humans, so it's up to us to put it right before it's too late – after all, we're not the only creatures living on Earth . . .

Don't forget the pets –

IN 1981 the R.S.P.C.A. re-housed 94,000 stray and unwanted *cats* and *dogs*! But it had to humanely destroy 134,000! This, of course, covered animals that were ill or injured in some way, but it included a very large proportion of abandoned pets for whom homes simply couldn't be found.

It doesn't take a genius to add up the two sets of figures and come out with a total of *over a quarter of a million* stray and abandoned animals in *one year*! That's more than the population of Iceland!

We asked the R.S.P.C.A. what advice it had for anyone thinking of having a pet. They told us, "Think very carefully several times before you buy.

"There are all sorts of things to take into consideration, like vets' fees, boarding fees if you're away, the amount the animal's going to eat, how expensive that's likely to be, how much the animal is going to grow and how much exercise it will need."

Just about everybody's heard stories of dogs thrown out of cars on motorways and left to fend for themselves, or un-neutered cats that have litter after litter of kittens because the owner thinks it would be "wrong" to deprive the animal of its natural function. But the R.S.P.C.A. pointed out that one female cat can produce literally hundreds of kittens. It's OK finding homes for the first five. But the next five . . . ? And the five after that . . . ? Suddenly you can all too easily see where 94,000 strays come from.

Puppy dogs' tales –

IF *you're* thinking of having a dog or a cat, bear one or two things in mind.

With a dog, for example, there's very little point in buying an Irish wolfhound if you live in a top-floor, three-roomed flat! Something the size of a wolfhound needs *space*!

Sounds obvious, but that cuddly little furry bundle of puppyhood will *grow*. It will also chew things, make puddles all over the place until it's properly house-trained, need worming at eight weeks old, inoculation against hardpad, distemper and canine hepatitis at six months, a licence (also at six months), a collar with an identity disc on it to be worn in public (maximum penalty if this isn't adhered to — £400), regular meals and regular exercise.

And that's just the beginning!

All dogs need a certain amount of training. They also need love and affection. A dog that isn't cared for properly is a very sorry animal.

They need grooming, and their claws may occasionally need clipping. And whether you like it or not, they definitely need a couple of decent walks a day!

So if you're the kind of person who's basically lazy and disorganised and doesn't like tramping across the park in all kinds of weather — *don't buy a dog!*

Be a practical cat –

CATS are a different proposition. At least you don't have to take 'em for walks, but it's perfectly possible you *will* have to rescue a moggy from one or other of the weird and wonderful places it'll get stuck in throughout its life!

The Observer Book of Pets, re-published

in 1980, estimated that Britain already has a stray cat population of more than *one million*. So if your heart's set on having a furry feline — *have it spayed or neutered!*

Kittens can be protected from two killer diseases — Feline Infectious Enteritis and Feline Influenza — by an injection at eight to nine weeks, a further injection at twelve weeks, and a yearly booster.

Cats can be extremely fussy eaters, so it's a good idea to give them a varied diet from a very early age. *Don't* fall into the trap, with any animal, of giving *too much* to eat. Cats and dogs, like people, can be greedy individuals, but overfeeding leads to fatness, and you really aren't doing the animal any favours, because you're actually shortening its life-span.

Going wild –

CATS, dogs and goldfish are probably the most usual pets in this country. But alligators, monkeys, pythons, parrots and even panthers have all been kept by aspiring owners, as well.

Exotic animals are fine in exotic places, and that's where they should stay. Sadly, though, that isn't always what happens. At one time alligators were actually thought to be *breeding* in the sewers of New York because people were buying baby ones as presents, and when the owners got fed up with them — they simply flushed 'em down the loo!

So if you're going to have a pet — choose one to suit your circumstances.

A goldfish'll be quite happy for a couple of days without any attention. A Shetland pony won't.

The R.S.P.C.A. publish various pamphlets on pets and pet-care. Write to them, enclosing a stamped, addressed envelope at: R.S.P.C.A. Headquarters, The Causeway, Horsham, Sussex.

Remember to enclose an S.A.E. when writing to any of the organisations listed below –

A short story
by Carol Gow

I WAS over the moon when Greg wrote to me, asking if I would like to spend a week with him and his family at the end of October. We'd met on holiday in Spain — an old story, I suppose.

Greg had already stayed at my house for a couple of weekends and we'd kept in touch constantly by phone and letter. The thought of spending a whole week with him in Scotland was wonderful — only Mum and Dad weren't so keen.

If you're an only child, then maybe you'll understand what it's like — Dad especially was always so over-protective, I'm sure he'd have been happier living in the Victorian age! To top it all, it was my birthday on the thirty-first of October.

"You'll be away for it," Mum said, as if it was the end of the world or something.

"I know," I sighed. "But I'd really like to go, Mum. I get so fed up never seeing him, and not being able to find a job doesn't help, exactly . . ."

Mum squeezed my hand.

"Stop worrying. You're not the only one who can't find work. Something will turn up soon."

I shrugged. I'd left school after the summer term full of hope, feeling sure that if I tried hard enough something would come up — but as each week went by I grew more and more discouraged, more and more defeated.

I think in the end, that's what clinched it. Both Mum and Dad knew I'd been pretty depressed and maybe they thought a week in Scotland would take my mind off things, buck me up. Mum phoned Greg's mum and that was it, all arranged.

I fell in love with Greg's home right away. It was a big white house right at the top end of the village, near the shore. At night, you could lie awake and hear the waves crashing against the rocks.

I liked his family, too. He had two sisters — Elaine and Vicki. His gran lived with them, too, and they all made such a fuss of me that I felt really welcome.

Greg had a week off work, and the first two days he took me round all the local beauty spots — and I took my sketch pad.

"Wouldn't a camera be a bit quicker?" he'd tease me whenever I spotted something that interested me.

"Anyone can take a snapshot," I'd say. "This is all mine . . ."

GREG planned a special treat for my birthday.

"Your birthday falls on Hallowe'en, Lisa," he said. "We can have a Hallowe'en party — a proper one, on the beach, complete with bonfire, turnip lanterns and toffee apples!"

We sat in the kitchen, making coffee and planning the party, and Greg told me about Hallowe'en and its superstitions.

"Hallowe'en — it's the night when the veil between this world and the next is lifted . . ." He paused and tried to look spooky. "The dead revisit their homes and kelpies, ghoulies and ghaisties walk . . ."

"What's a kelpie?" I asked him.

"A spirit of the water," he whispered in my ear.

"Stop it — you're sending shivers

46

Dark Future

running up and down my spine," I said. Vicki came in just then. "I came to find out what you're planning for this Hallowe'en thing." She bit into an apple and looked at me. "Born on Hallowe'en, Lisa?" She whistled. "Round here they'd say you had second sight — that those born on Hallowe'en can see things denied to other mortals . . ."

She was having me on, and I laughed. "Well, my second sight tells me . . ." I paused . . . "that the milk is boiling over!" And we both laughed as Greg rescued the pan from the stove.

On my birthday, Hallowe'en, Greg and I spent the afternoon collecting driftwood on the shingle beach and building a fire. After tea, everyone else joined us.

The bay was beautiful enough by day — the water was a deep, deep blue, foamy and frothy white where it hit the jagged rocks on either side. But as dusk approached, it grew even more beautiful. We lit the fire and watched it blaze and I sighed as Greg put his arms round me. It had been such a lovely day.

I looked round the little sheltered cove and I knew that I wanted to try to capture some of it on paper. I picked up my sketch pad and Greg made as if to come with me, but I shook my head. "No — you look after the sausages — I won't be long."

I WALKED along the shingle and edged past an outcrop of rock towards Kelpie's Pool. Greg had shown it to me on my first day — a dark, deep, bottomless pool — so dark and so deep that even on the sunniest day, no shadow or reflection had ever been seen in it.

I sat by the edge, sketching quickly, my fingers trembling as I managed to capture something of the dark, shadowy rocks against the night sky — managed to capture the way they looked almost alive and breathing . . .

Then, quite suddenly, I stopped sketching and looked up, as if someone had called my name. But I'd *heard* nothing, rather I'd *felt* it. There was no-one there.

I leaned forward and there was a movement across the water. A figure. I caught my breath. It was my reflection. As I leaned forward, my long, blonde hair hung straight across the water. Yet Greg had said there was never any reflection . . .

There was a sudden movement on the surface of the water, a ripple, starting small and then cascading outwards in an ever-widening circle, and for a moment the reflection was broken into jagged pieces of moonlight scattered on the water. Then, suddenly, the water became completely still again and I stared at the girl with the long hair once more — only this time there was someone behind her.

It was a boy — and in my mind I could hear him calling me. He wasn't just a shadow, or a reflection. It was as if he was flesh and blood — as real as Greg. Somehow I knew his eyes were blue — deep blue like the water in the bay on a sunny day. I leaned forward, pulled irresistibly by those eyes. The rock under my foot tilted and I slithered forward, off-balance. I knew I was falling, but I wasn't frightened. It was as if everything was happening in slow motion, as if I was outside myself, watching it happen, as if to someone else . . .

T HE water closed around me but it wasn't cold. It felt strangely warm, warm and gentle, and welcoming. Like the voice I'd heard in my mind — the boy's voice. The kelpie's voice — the spirit of the water.

Suddenly there was shouting and the water was foaming and churning round me. Someone grabbed me and at that instant the water turned icy cold.

The next thing I knew I was in Greg's kitchen. His gran made me a hot drink and I was hustled out of my wet things and into a hot steamy bath.

"I shouldn't have let you wander off," he said when we were alone. "It was my fault. I know you don't realise how dangerous the rocks can be at night." He touched my cheek. "When I carried you back to the house you were talking about a boy in the pool." He smiled. "My fault for filling your head full of superstitions. I didn't mean to frighten you, Lisa."

"Forget it," I said. "Let's pretend it never happened."

Set against the rest of that wonderful week, the incident didn't seem important. It faded against the other memories I took home with me; memories of being with Greg, of falling more and more in love with him, of a perfect holiday.

When I got home, I discovered I started missing Greg and Scotland almost from the first minute. I unpacked and leafed through my sketches, remembering the places Greg had shown me.

Suddenly I came across the half-finished sketch of Kelpie's Pool. I barely glanced at it and yet something in the idea of the shadows caught my eye and held it. My hand trembled and the paper shook. It was almost like a figure — a figure with an arm raised, beckoning.

Q UICKLY, I crushed the sketch into a ball and threw it to the other side of the room. I didn't understand any of what had happened that night. Maybe I didn't want to understand. It was something I just wanted to blot out of my mind completely.

I forgot all about Kelpie's Pool until yesterday. I'd just finished a long letter to Greg, thanking him for my birthday present, telling him I wished it had been possible for us to spend my birthday together, like last year, when a letter arrived in the lunch-time post.

He'd enclosed a cutting from the local paper. A young girl had been drowned in Kelpie's Pool. She'd apparently been walking her dog and slipped on the rocks . . . There was a photograph of her. She was young, about my age, with long blonde hair just like mine.

"I was so frightened when I read it," Greg had written. "I suppose because I suddenly realised it could have been you. I still haven't forgiven myself for being such a fool and letting you wander off on your own like that . . ."

I stopped reading there and held my breath.

I stared at the picture of the girl . . . *could have been you, could have been you . . .*

Maybe now I understood. I'd stared into the pool and I'd thought I'd been seeing my own reflection. Now, sitting here with the cutting in front of me, with the photo of a girl with long blonde hair just like mine, I'm scared. Because now I know I wasn't seeing the present at all. I wasn't seeing my own reflection. Maybe I was seeing *her* reflection . . . Maybe I was seeing the future . . .

A TOUCH OF CLASS!

Accessories can make or break an outfit. If you're unsure about what "goes," stick to the classic looks we show you here!

Legs go!

All tied up, chained and pinned!

Plain and pearly!

Ribbons rule!

Slant it!

LOVE ON THE AIRWAVES

That evening—

The following day I was allowed up—

50

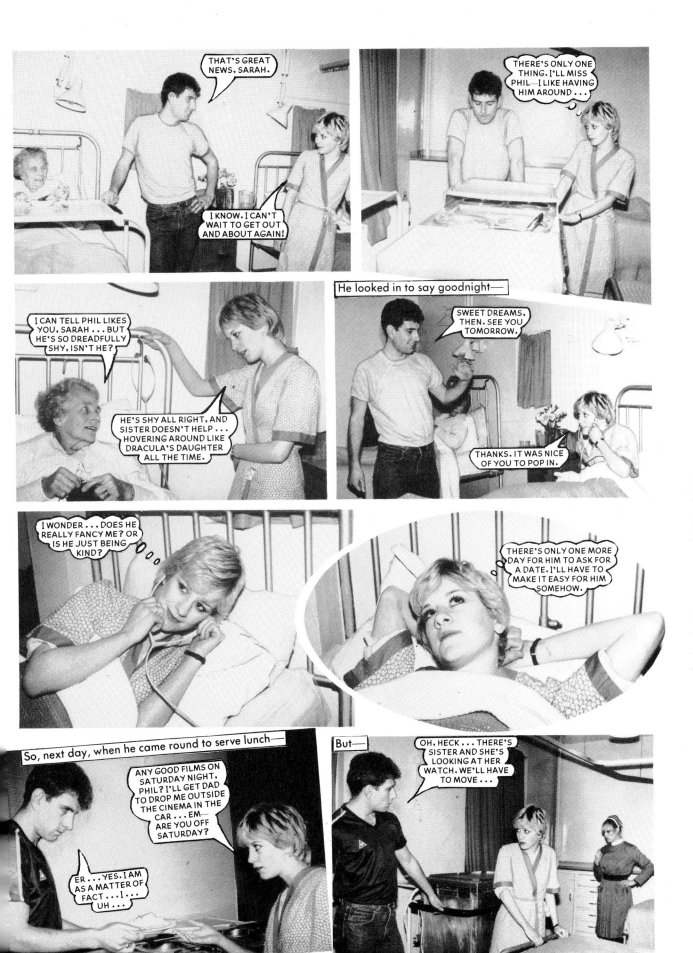

I SUPPOSE SO—BUT DO YOU KNOW IF THERE'RE ANY GOOD FILMS ON?

OH, YES... THE ODEON SHOULD BE GOOD... BUT GET THAT NEXT PLATE READY...

For the rest of the afternoon, it was like trying to catch an express train—

SORRY, CAN'T STOP! I'M NEEDED AT RECEPTION.

SISTER SOURPUSS IS TO BLAME. HE'S SCARED TO SPEAK TO ME.

And as the time wore on—

I'VE GOT TO DO SOMETHING! I'M NOT LEAVING HERE WITHOUT A DATE! I'VE GOT TO GIVE HIM TIME!

AAA...OOOOOH!

A nurse helped me back to bed. Then sourpuss and a doctor came on the scene—

HMM... HER PULSE IS NORMAL.

MMM...OOOH! I FEEL SO WEAK...

I THINK WE'D BETTER KEEP HER A DAY OR TWO MORE.

HMPH! IF YOU SAY SO.

IT'S WORKED!

After a while, though, it got boring—

I'LL LISTEN TO THE HOSPITAL RADIO. I WISH SHE WOULDN'T KEEP LOOKING AT ME LIKE THAT, THOUGH.

COULD I HAVE A WORD WITH YOU, ORDERLY?

SHE'S CERTAINLY TELLING HIM OFF. AND BY THE WAY HE'S LOOKING DOWN HERE IT MUST BE MY FAULT.

Shortly afterwards, the patient's request programme got underway—

...AND NOW FOR THE GIRL WITH THE SPARKLING EYES IN WARD 8... ADAM AND THE ANTS...

WHO'S THE LUCKY GIRL?

He played more records after that.

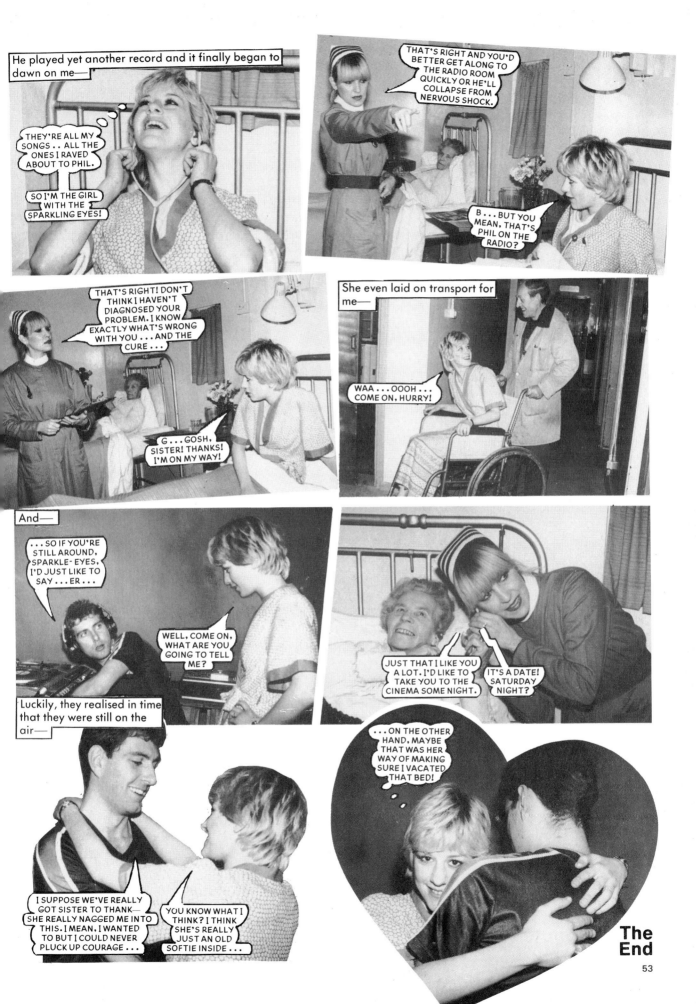

The End

53

WHO DO YOU THINK YOU ARE?

Perhaps you think you know yourself quite well, but it's almost certain that your family and friends look at you in a completely different light! If you'd like to get a bit closer to the real you, find out what your faults are and learn how to put them right, just read on!

Thumbs Up!

1. Have a look at your thumb, then compare it with the various types described below and find out what this points to in your personality! Is it . . .
- a. . . . waisted, narrowing in the middle?
- b. . . . stiff and inflexible?
- c. . . . pointed when you look at it from the side?
- d. . . . square?
- e. . . . almond shaped?

Take A Break . . .

2. At last! Entering all those competitions on the backs of cornflake packets has finally paid off, and you've been offered your ideal dream holiday absolutely free! Would you choose . . .
- a. . . . a fortnight on a faraway island in the sun?
- b. . . . a romantic cruise on a luxury liner?
- c. . . . an exciting stay in a big city?
- d. . . . a skiing holiday, high in the Alps?
- e. . . . to travel from one place to another until the money ran out?

Body Talk!

3. Do you always fall for tall, skinny guys or do you go more for short, cuddly types? Have a look at the list of basic types below and choose the one which sounds most like your ideal guy. Is he . . .
- a. . . . broad and well built?
- b. . . . plump, perhaps a bit overweight?
- c. . . . tall, lean and wiry?
- d. . . . small and slim with long legs?

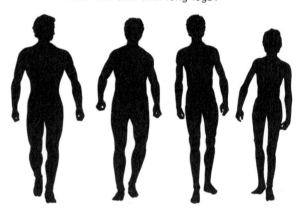

The Name Of The Game!

4. A name can say a lot about a person, and the name you'd choose for your ideal guy can say a lot about him — and about *you*. Choose your favourite from the list we've given below and find out what's in a name.
- a. David.
- b. John.
- c. Gareth.
- d. Steve.
- e. Shaun.

Sign Here!

5. When you sign your name, do you . . .
- a. . . . underline it with a curve?

Jane Smith

- b. . . . put a circle round it?

Ann Hill

- c. . . . use particularly large capital letters?

Angela Brown

- d. . . . make it larger than your normal handwriting?

my handwriting
Carol Parkinson

- e. . . . use tapering, thread-like strokes?

Susan Goodman

The Shape Of Things To Come!

6. From the five simple shapes pictured here, pick the one which most appeals to you and find out how you shape up to romance!
  a. A figure of 8.
  b. A square.
  c. A heart.
  d. A triangle.
  e. Crossed sticks.

Now turn to the conclusions and all will be revealed!

CONCLUSIONS

1a) This shows that you've got very strong will-power and like to have your own way.
1b) You have an obstinate streak which means that you don't really care much for change and adventure.
1c) You know how to charm the birds from the trees, and you can twist people round your little finger!
1d) You're emotionally cautious and you rarely make hasty decisions or do anything without working it out carefully in advance.
1e) This means that you're creative and artistic.

2a) What a dreamer you are! You're a real romantic and if you do make it to your dream-island, you'll fall in love with the beautiful scenery and gorgeous sunsets, but you'll definitely need someone special by your side to make it perfect!
2b) There's a hint of vanity in your personality and you love showing off glamorous clothes and being pampered and fussed over. Could be there's a hidden actress in you clamouring to be let out!
2c) You're just a little bit cautious about trying new things, and although you enjoy seeing out-of-the-ordinary places, you also like to feel safe and in the middle of things. A couple of weeks in Paris with a friend would be ideal for you.
2d) You're packed with energy and enthusiasm so lying in the sun for a fortnight would bore you to tears! You're not too keen on dressing up and like to be active and slightly daring on your holidays, so flying down the sunlit slopes would suit you down to the ground!
2e) If you picked this as your ideal holiday, then you're looking for adventure with a capital A! You love a challenge and a feeling of freedom, so you long to explore strange places and travel as widely as possible. Wherever you go, you'll certainly make the most of it.

3a) You're very feminine and you love to be looked after and made a fuss of. Watch out for the competition, though, 'cos this guy's pretty popular and usually has lots of girls in tow. If you want him, you'll have to fight for him!
3b) You probably have strong links with your home and family and you expect him to feel the same. He's kind, friendly and fun to be with, but you WILL have to put up with having his mates around, even if you're not too keen on them, 'cos his friends definitely mean a lot to him.
3c) He's likely to be quite thoughtful and serious. As you're probably the outdoor, sporty type with a liking for fresh air and exercises it might take you a while to get used to his quiet, serious hobbies!
3d) This shows that he's got lots of energy and you may have quite a job to keep up with him! You're looking for friendship and affection rather than a Great Romance, and you like to have a shoulder to lean on. This guy could well be just right for you.

4a) You're not at all keen on being liberated and independent. In fact, all you really want is someone to love and rely on who'll be able to protect you from the big, bad world. You're not terribly ambitious and you'll probably devote yourself to making a home rather than a career.
4b) You need a comfortable, friendly and affectionate boyfriend who won't row and cause arguments. You like to have a quiet, secure sort of life and so you tend to play safe in romance. Danger and adventure hold no attraction for you!

4c) You love action and excitement and you're also a bit head-strong and impulsive, which can get you into hot water at times. You can be very secretive, especially where romance is concerned, and you like to keep people guessing.
4d) You're bright, happy-go-lucky and very modern. You love going out and meeting unusual people and you're probably pretty keen on pop music and dancing the night away at the local disco as well. Popular, lively and a little bit crazy, you're still an old-fashioned romantic at heart.
4e) You like to be different, you take both friendship and romance very seriously and you don't really like discussing your relationships with anyone else. You've got a strong sense of fate, believing that what will be will be . . . and this includes your love-life!

5a) This means you need a lot of admiration and attention. You love to be in love — usually with the best-looking guy around!
5b) It could be that you are shy and need to come out of your shell a bit. Watch out that you aren't missing out on all the fun by standing on the outside looking in. People want to get to know you, so give them a chance!
5c) This is a sign of a highly-developed ego and a sense of drama. You love to be recognised and stared at, and your social life is probably active, varied and very exciting!
5d) You like to impress people and yet underneath you are really quite reserved and even a little shy. You might well be fighting an inferiority complex — and you're winning, too!
5e) This shows that you are very good at getting your own way, and that just by employing a few of your wiles, you can persuade people to do practically anything.

6a) You aren't as easy-going as you could be, you tend to take life a bit too seriously and try too hard to make people like you. Relax and learn to laugh at yourself more – you'll be amazed at how much happier you become!
6b) You're friendly and sociable but a little bit shy, and although you sometimes feel trapped, you don't have the courage to meet new faces and go to different places on your own. All you really need is a push in the right direction from a close friend, so let someone know how you feel and your life could soon be much more exciting!
6c) Oh boy, are you a romantic! You'd happily spend the whole day dreaming and you let your heart rule your head every time! You probably fall in and out of love twice a week, and each time you're convinced that it's the Real Thing! Whatever life holds for you, it certainly won't be dull!
6d) You're a very positive, slightly aggressive person and you want to be first in everything, whether it's clothes, music, make-up or romance! You're also very bright and quick to pick up on new ideas so you almost invariably succeed!
6e) You're naturally rather nervous and you sometimes feel that your family don't understand you and that the whole world's out to get at you! If you can channel all that energy into strenuous activities like sports or games of some kind, you'll find that you become far less resentful and you MIGHT even become a star!

Fit is Fun!

Winter is no time for lying around dreaming of summer. Do something and that sunshine you're waiting for will be here before you know it!

COME on — stop huddling under all those blankets, clutching your hotty! Just because it's winter, doesn't mean to say you have to hibernate. Probably the last thing you have on your mind on a freezing winter morning is any form of exercise whatsoever, but we're about to change your mind!

In winter, it's all too easy to come home from school or work, pile on three jumpers and two pairs of socks and slump in front of the fire, doing nothing more strenuous than reaching for another chocolate. But think ahead! When spring has finally sprung, you'll need to be fit in order to be able to speed away from the hordes of handsome hunks who'll be pursuing you all over town!

There are loads of things you can do in winter-time to keep fit and healthy — and you'll feel much better for it, we promise! Try some of these for starters!

SKIING

There's one sport which immediately comes into most people's minds in winter-time — and that's skiing.

Skiing fanatics will vouch for the fact that there's nothing more exhilarating than flying down the side of a mountain under a clear, blue sky and a brilliant sun.

Though it can be a costly sport if you are buying all your own equipment, lots of people hire everything they need from ski-schools and sports shops for a reasonable fee. All you need after you've got all the gear is a bit of courage — and a sense of adventure!

Many activity centres and some schools have dry ski slopes where you can learn the basics of the sport before you risk heading for the white stuff.

It's a good idea to find out if there are any such ski slopes in your area — your district or community council or local tourist information office will be able to tell you.

Most activity centres organise skiing holidays to places such as the Aviemore Centre in Scotland or farther afield to Switzerland, France and Austria.

If you tend to fall a bit too often, you can always console yourself with the thought of the après-ski — who knows who you might meet there!

SKATING

Another popular winter sport is skating and most large towns have their own ice-skating rink, which is generally open from October through till March. They have evening and weekend skating sessions which last for around two hours.

Charges vary according to whether the session is full ice or just end ice, where only part of the rink is in use. For a full ice Saturday evening session, you'd normally pay around 95p entry fee, plus 40p to hire ice-skating boots.

In addition to having a laugh when you fall over and laughing at everyone else doing the same, there's normally a D.J. playing the latest hits for you to dance to (or fall around to!). Skating rinks are great places for making friends — you can't seem to avoid bumping into people!

If you get fed up making a fool of yourself, many rinks have instructors who, for a fee of around £2.50 an hour, will teach you how to stay upright — maybe you'll even progress to a dazzling display of twirls and leaps and really show up your mates! You never know, you might

If you're still at school, it'll cost you about 70p to join and something like 15p an evening after that. These prices also apply if you're unemployed. The classes usually last for 1½-2 hours and the most popular ones tend to be the most energetic ones.

Amongst the courses on offer are keep fit, contemporary dance and badminton, as well as more unusual things like the martial arts, fencing, canoeing, etc.

and can stretch easily into any position you want them to.

DANCE AND KEEP FIT

Contemporary dance and keep fit both involve exercising and dancing to music and are great classes to join with friends — you can all laugh at each other's attempts!

THE MARTIAL ARTS

The martial arts such as judo, karate, jujitsu and so on often have

have hidden talents and turn out to be the next female ice-skating champion of the world!

Don't forget roller-skating, too, which has recently enjoyed a revival — quite a few ice-skating rinks have gone over to roller-skating instead. At least you don't get wet when you fall, as you do with ice-skating!

JOGGING

You're probably laughing your head off at the thought of jogging in winter. Although this has become one of the most popular ways of keeping fit in this country, lots of people are fair-weather joggers and at the least sign of rain or cold they won't bother going out.

But if you can possibly manage to force yourself to get up half an hour earlier in the mornings and go for a short jog around the block before school or work, you'll find it really wakes you up and makes you feel alert and bright — you might even enjoy school when you get there!

Don't overdo it, though. Sometimes you get a false sense of your own stamina the first time you go out. After ten minutes you'll probably feel really tired, then from nowhere you get a sudden burst of energy and feel as if you could go on for a good few hundred yards more — *don't!*

Start very gently, and build up slowly over a few weeks to a maximum time of 30 minutes. Try to pace yourself so you don't go so fast you get tired, or so slow you get bored. Happy jogging!

GROUP ACTIVITIES

Winter's the time when evening classes at colleges, schools and community centres get into swing and there are so many different things on offer that there's absolutely no excuse for not joining at least one of them.

Being a teenager means you can learn many new things at a very small cost to yourself, except for the aching muscles you may have at first.

YOGA

Yoga is a fairly recent addition to the evening class syllabus but it's become so popular it's often one of the first classes to fill up, so if you want to secure a place, join early!

Yoga is also an activity you can practise alone at home and you will be advised by your yoga teacher to do this every day for a few minutes so that your muscles become relaxed

special classes on self-defence for women which could come in handy and will make you feel a lot safer.

SOMETHING DIFFERENT

Learning something completely different, like canoeing or fencing, can lead to you taking part in competitions with other centres if you're very good, and in the case of canoeing, you may even get the chance of weekends away.

Find out about all these activities by keeping an eye on your local newspaper, or phone your district or community council for information.

CUSHY NUMBERS!

continued from page 22.

YOU'LL NEED . . .

WOOL: Pingouin Pingoland, 50 g balls.
NEEDLES — A pair of 6 mm (No. 4).
TENSION — 12 sts and 16 rows to 10 cm (4 in.) square.
ABBREVIATIONS — K — Knit; P — Purl; st(s) — stitch(es); cont — continue; comm — commencing; st-st — stocking-stitch (1 row knit, 1 row purl); g-st — garter-stitch (every row knit); inc — increase by working into front and back of stitch; dec — decrease by working 2 stitches together; beg — beginning; alt — alternate; tog — together.

WAISTCOAT

WOOL — 5 balls purple, 1 ball pale blue and 1 ball red.
PLUS — 3 silver buttons, 3 blue shirt buttons, 40 cm of silver ric-rac, foam chippings.
TO MAKE — With purple, cast on 49 sts.
Row 1 — K26, P1, K22.
Row 2 — P22, K1, P26.
Repeat rows 1 and 2 nine more times (20 rows).
Row 21 — K4, P1, (K1, P1) six times, K9, P1, K5, P1, (K1, P1) six times, K4.
Row 22 — P4, K1, (P1, K1) six times, P5, K1, P9, K1, (P1, K1) six times, P4.
Repeat rows 21 and 22 once more.
Row 25 — K4, P13, K9, P1, K5, P13, K4.
Comm with row 2, repeat rows 2 and 1 six more times, then row 2 once more (38 rows worked from cast on).
Next row — K24 purple, K1 blue, K24 purple, using separate balls of wool for each colour change.

Next and every following alt row: P in same colours as previous row.
Next row — K23 purple, K3 blue, K23 purple.
Cont in this manner, increasing blue sts by 2 every K row until following row has been worked: P12 purple, P25 blue, P12 purple.
Cont in st-st with purple and comm with a K row.
Work 64 rows.
Cast off.

COLLAR —
(Make 2).
With blue, cast on 13 sts and cont in st-st comm with a K row.
Work 2 rows.
Dec 1 st at beg and end of next and every following row until 3 sts remain.
P3 tog. Cast off.

BOW TIE — With red, cast on 5 sts and cont in g-st. *K 2 rows.
Inc 1 st at beg of next and every following row until there are 11 sts on the needle.
K 6 rows.
Dec 1 st at beg of next and every following row until 5 sts remain.
K 2 rows.*
Repeat from * to * once more.
Cast off.
With red, cast on 3 sts and work 12 rows g-st.
Cast off.

TO MAKE UP — Sew in ends of yarn. Fold waistcoat in half and sew side seams. Stuff with chippings and join base. Sew on collar, attaching points with cast off yarn. Sew bow tie together, covering centre with knitted strip. Sew to neck. Sew on buttons. Loop ric-rac from pockets to button and catch down with a few stitches.

DOMINOES

WOOL — 4 balls in black and 1 ball in ivory.
PLUS — Foam chippings.
Backs — (Make 4). With black, cast on 18 sts and work in st-st comm with a K row.
Work 42 rows.
Cast off.
FRONTS — (Make 4). With black, cast on 18 sts and cont in st-st comm with a K row.
Work 20 rows.
Work 2 rows K in ivory.
Work 20 rows st-st comm with a K row in black.
Cast off.

BOBBLES — (Make 28). With ivory, cast on 1 st and K into front and back twice (4 sts).
Next row — P.
Next row — K.
Next row — P.

Next row — (K 2 tog) twice, slip first st over second st, break yarn and draw thread through st.

TO MAKE UP — Sew bobbles to fronts in same order as photograph by passing threads to wrong side and knotting. Take 1 back and 1 front and sew round 3 sides, stuff with chippings and sew remaining side. Sew the 4 dominoes together as shown.

CLOCK

WOOL — 2 balls yellow and 2 balls red, and a small amount of jade.
PLUS — Foam chippings.
BACK — With red, cast on 17 sts and cont in st-st comm with a K row.
Work 2 rows.
Cast on 3 sts at beg of next 4 rows (29 sts).
Cast on 2 sts at beg of next 4 rows (37 sts).
Inc 1 st at beg of next 12 rows (49 sts)*.
Work 20 rows.
**Dec 1 st at beg of next 12 rows (37 sts).
Cast off 2 sts at beg of next 4 rows (29 sts).
Cast off 3 sts at beg of next 4 rows (17 sts).
Work 2 rows.
Cast off.

FRONT — With yellow as back to *.
Work 5 rows.
Work hands as follows, using separate balls of wool for each colour change.
Row 1 — P 22 yellow, P5 red, P22 yellow.
Row 2 — K21 yellow, K7 red, K21 yellow.
Rows 3 and 7 — P20 yellow, P9 red, P20 yellow.
Rows 4 and 8 — K20 yellow, K9 red, K20 yellow.
Row 5 — P3 yellow, P37 red, P9 yellow.
Row 6 — K9 yellow, K37 red, K3 yellow.
Row 9 — P21 yellow, P7 red, P21 yellow.
Row 10 — K22 yellow, K5 red, K22 yellow.
Cont in yellow and work 5 rows.
Cont as for back from ** to end.

TO MAKE UP — Sew in ends of thread. Take front and back pieces and sew all round, leaving a space open. Stuff with chippings and join opening. With jade wool, embroider 12, 3, 6 and 9 in chain stitch. Make 8 bobbles in jade as for dominoes and sew in place, as shown.

BIGGER THAN USUAL

POP·WORD

Here's a Popword which will keep you entertained through the long winter nights! It's all about Christmassy things and famous people, and just to help you, we've filled in the darker lines.

There's no prize for this one — you'll find the answers on page 80 — but no peeking until you've finished!

1. On the Eleventh day of Christmas there were eleven ------ -------.
2. "Rock On, Tommy" was the catch phrase for this TV twosome.
3. A well-known carol about a quiet evening.
4. His "Newsround" can be seen on BBC.
5. Ali Baba's enemies.
6. She sang the theme for the film, "For Your Eyes Only."
7. People might do this outside your front door at Christmas.
8. He had a "Madhouse" on TV.
9. This Crackerjack duo are "fandabidozi"!
10. You go to the theatre to see this show at Christmas.
11. Adam Ant's real name.
12. He goes out and about swapping on "Swap Shop."
13. The night before you open your pressies.
14. The Radio 1 DJ with the Christmas name.
15. Gold, myrrh and ----------- were the three gifts of the Magi.
16. Sting's real name.
17. Tony Hadley is the lead singer with this group.
18. This pantomime 'male' is played by a girl!
19. She's the presenter on "Tiswas."
20. Where "The Babes" can be found.
21. Simon Le Bon is the lead singer with this group.
22. These get hung around your house at Christmas.
23. Bob Geldof's group.
24. Add "Fingers" for an Irish group.
25. He looked out on the feast of Stephen.
26. Chrissie Hynde's group.
27. ITV's film series, introduced by Chris Kelly.
28. Where the partridge can be found at Christmas!

1	P	I	P	E	R	S	P	I	P	I	N	G	
2	C	A	N	N	O	N	A	N	D	B	A	L	L
3			S	I	L	E	N	T	N	I	G	H	T
4				J	O	H	N	C	R	A	V	E	N
5	F	O	R	T	Y	T	H	I	E	V	E	S	
6	S	H	E	E	N	A	E	A	S	T	O	N	
7		C	A	R	O	L	S	I	N	G	I	N	G
8		R	O	S	S	A	B	B	O	T			
9			T	H	E	K	R	A	N	K	I	E	S
10	P	A	N	T	O	M	I	M	E				
11	S	T	U	A	R	T	G	O	D	D	A	R	D
12	K	I	E	T	H	C	H	E	G	W	I	N	
13		C	H	R	I	S	T	M	A	S	E	V	E
14		N	O	E	L	E	D	M	O	N	D	S	
15	F	R	A	N	K	I	N	C	E	N	S	E	
16	G	O	R	D	O	N	S	U	M	N	E	R	
17	S	P	A	N	D	A	U	B	A	L	L	E	T
18													
19		S	A	L	L	Y	J	A	M	E	S		
20	I	N	T	H	E	W	O	O	D				
21	D	U	R	A	N	D	U	R	A	N			
22		D	E	C	O	R	A	T	I	O	N	S	
23	B	O	O	M	T	O	W	N	R	A	T	S	
24	S	T	I	F	F	L	I	T	T	L	E		
25	K	O	O	G	W	E	N	C	E	L	A	S	
26			P	R	E	T	E	N	D	E	R	S	
27		C	L	A	P	P	E	R	B	O	A	R	D
28	P	A	R	A	E	A	T	R	E	E			

(Vertical word: PATCHES BRIGHTEN UP YOUR WINTER)

69

It's an "offal" life stuck here amongst the middle neck and scrag. If it wasn't for my film star impersonations, I'd go mad . . .

. . . I put on my Groucho Marx moustache and launched into my act . . .

WITH YOU IN A MINUTE, LADY. I GOTTA STRAIGHTEN THE ZIPS ON THE BLACK PUDDINGS.

HEY, THAT'S GOOD! AREN'T YOU THAT KARL MARX FELLOW WHO USED TO BE IN FILMS?

KARL MARX—I ASK YOU! MY TALENT'S WASTED HERE . . .

WHAT'S UP WITH HIM THEN? WHAT DID I SAY?

And when she'd gone . . .

NEVER MIND, GUS—SHE GOT THE GENERAL IDEA. ANYHOW, YOUR MUM SAYS NOT TO FORGET THE BACON FOR YOUR DAD'S TEA.

OK, MILLIE. I WON'T FORGET.

Millie was the girl next door . . .

AH, WELL, THAT'S SHOW BUSINESS, I GUESS —ONE MINUTE YOU'RE UP THERE WITH THE SIDES OF HAM AND THE NEXT YOU'RE DOWN WITH THE TRIPE 'N' THE DRIPPING.

On my way home . . .

HAAAH—WHOA UP THERE. I AIN'T SEEN THAT FILLY AROUND AFORE, PARDNER . . .

I WOULDN'T MIND GETTING TO KNOW HER—WONDER WHAT'S INTERESTING HER SO MUCH?

Me In The Movies!

HEY, IT'S A NOTICE FOR A NEW FILM CLUB! MAYBE WE'RE TWO OF A KIND—MAYBE SHE'S BEEN NUTS ABOUT FILMS SINCE SHE WAS KNEE-HIGH TO JOHN WAYNE'S SPURS. JUST LIKE ME...

...WE COULD HAVE FANTASTIC TIMES TALKING ABOUT BOGEY AND ROBERT REDFORD—FILMS COULD BE OUR COMMON BOND!

The only thing was, when I came out of my dream she was gone—and, anyhow, I'd arranged to take Millie to a party that night...

That was one of my things—dressing up in something crazy to go to a party. It always got a great laugh...

GUS...ARE YOU READY YET?

...YEEEE...AAAAH!

SO YOU THOUGHT YOU WERE GOING TO A PARTY, WELL YOU'RE WRONG—TODAY MILLIE MITCHELL, THIS IS YOUR DEATH...

YOU'LL HAVE ME A NERVOUS WRECK, GUS. WHY ARE YOU SO CRAZY?

IT'S THE BIG STAR IN ME TRYING TO GET OUT, MILLIE...YOU BRING OUT THE BEST IN ME.

WOOO...OH!

THE BEST IN HIM! I JUST WISH HE'D TAKE ME SERIOUSLY—AND NOT JUST AS AN AUDIENCE FOR HIS NEW IDEAS!

My 'mummy' act went down well. But I couldn't quite believe my luck...

IT—IT'S HER!

YEEEEEK!

YOU'RE THE CASUALTY IN "CATCH 22", AREN'T YOU? I MEAN, YOU COULDN'T BE ANYTHING AS UNSUBTLE AS A MUMMY.

IN ACTUAL FACT, I CUT MY FINGER AND DEVELOPED BLOOD POISONING.

BUT THAT WAS THE ANSWER OF A TRUE FILM BUFF. INTERESTED IN FILMS, ARE YOU?

OH, YES—I'VE JUST JOINED THE LOCAL FILM SOCIETY. HAYLIE'S MY NAME—HAYLIE MILNE.

She even had a name like a film star!

BUT, THAT'S GREAT! I'M JOINING TOO. I LIKE ALL SORTS OF FILMS— LAUREL AND HARDY, JAMES BOND, THE CARRY ON FILMS . . .

REALLY? HOW INTERESTING . . .

LIKE TO DANCE?

I THINK HE MEANS YOU . . .

WHO IS THAT?

OH, THAT'S GUS HAMILTON. HE COMES FROM A LONG LINE OF IDIOTS.

Unfortunately, she stuck with him for the rest of the evening . . .

LOOKS LIKE SHE LOST INTEREST, GUS . . .

NO—NO, WE'VE GOT A COMMON INTEREST IN FILMS. THAT BLOKE MIGHT HAVE WON TONIGHT . . . BUT, I BET SHE'LL THINK HE'S DEAD DULL WHEN SHE GETS TO KNOW HIM.

And when it was time to leave . . .

SEE YOU AT THE FILM CLUB.

OH . . . ER . . . YES, PROBABLY.

I couldn't wait for the film club night to come along.

SHE'S THE MOST WONDERFUL GIRL I'VE EVER SEEN! A SORT OF CROSS BETWEEN ALI McGRAW AND BROOKE SHIELDS.

It was Millie who spotted an advert in the paper for film extras for a spoof western . . .

IT'S JUST THE THING FOR YOU, GUS—FILL UP THIS FORM AND I'LL SEND IT OFF FOR YOU.

HEY, THANKS, MILLIE— FANTASTIC!

I WON'T HALF IMPRESS HAYLIE IF I GET THE JOB . . .

On the night of the film society meeting, I was really excited . . .

IT'S A JAPANESE FILM, SO WHY DON'T I GIVE THEM A BIT OF COLOUR LIKE THEY DO AT PREMIERES? FILM LOVERS'LL APPRECIATE THAT.

. . . ARRA . . . HONOULABLE JAPANESE MAN COME SEE WUNNILFULL FILM . . . DESIRE SEAT BESIDE BEAUTIFUL GIRL CALLED HAYLIE . . .

ER . . . UH . . . UM. GO RIGHT IN, MR . . . ER . . . UH . . .

HI, IT'S ME, GUS!

UH—ER—H- HELLO.

IS IT MY IMAGINATION? HAS SHE MOVED HER SEAT AWAY FROM ME . . . . . . NO, I MUST BE MISTAKEN.

It was one of the worst films I'd ever seen . . .

WHEN D' WE GET SOME ACTION . . . A BIT OF THE OLD KUNG FU?

IT ISN'T THAT KIND OF FILM. BESIDES, KUNG FU IS CHINESE, NOT JAPANESE.

Afterwards, a lot of pretty boring people stood around and discussed the film . . .

THE STORY HINTED ESSENTIALLY ON THE HERO'S BIZARRE FLIGHTS FROM REALITY— THE THEMATIC PATTERNS WERE ENTIRELY GERMANE TO OUR MODERN TIMES.

MOST FREUDIAN, IN FACT.

WHAT A LOAD OF RUBBISH!

I BEG YOUR PARDON. I DON'T THINK YOU UNDERSTAND, MR . . . ER . . . UM . . .

I KNOW THIS MUCH. THAT FILM WAS AN INSULT TO GOOD ENTERTAIN- MENT. IT WAS BORING.

They looked at me like I was the beast from the swamp . . .

HOW NAIVE! NOT ALL FILMS ARE MEANT TO ENTERTAIN . . . MAYBE LAUREL AND HARDY IS MORE IN YOUR LINE.

YEAH—AT LEAST YOU GET SOME ENJOYMENT FROM THEM—WHICH IS MORE THAN YOU'LL GET FROM THAT JAPANESE DROSS . . . GOODNIGHT!

It would've been nice to have made a dignified exit, but I tripped over my kimono . . .

AAAGH!

I felt terrible . . .

I'VE MADE A PROPER FOOL OF MYSELF. THOSE PEOPLE ARE EDUCATED—THEY REALLY KNOW ABOUT FILMS. I'VE NEVER EVEN HEARD OF THEMATIC PATTERNS 'N' STUFF . . .

HI, GUS—YOU LOOK LIKE SOMETHING JAWS SPAT OUT.

I'VE JUST HAD A SLIGHT UPSET . . . IT'S NOTHING, REALLY . . .

But I had to tell someone what had happened . . .

OH, POOR GUS—FORGET ABOUT THAT LOT! YOU'VE GOT MORE FILM KNOWLEDGE IN YOUR BIG TOE THAN THE LOT OF THEM PUT TOGETHER.

YEAH, BUT WHAT'S " STAR WARS " COMPARED TO " WAR AND PEACE " AND ALL THEM KEN RUSSELL THINGS THEY WATCH?

Maybe it was then I began to really see Millie for the first time . . .

MAYBE THEY'RE THE ONES THAT DO ALL THE ACTING AND PRETENDING, GUS. YOU'RE THE ONE WITH A GENUINE LOVE OF THE CINEMA.

YOU—YOU THINK SO, MILLIE?

Then, a few weeks later . . .

HEY, MILLIE—MILLIE! IT'S COME! I'VE BEEN ACCEPTED AS AN EXTRA FOR THAT FILM!

OH, GUS, THAT'S GREAT!

GOOD LUCK, GUS!

THANKS, KID—FOR EVERYTHING! IT AIN'T EASY FOR A HOMBRE LIKE ME TO TELL A GAL WHAT HE THINKS OF HER—BUT—BUT YOU JES' LAID A SPECIAL BRANDIN' IRON ON MY HEART.

. . . maybe a new star was about to rise up in the cinema world—but, one thing was sure, the gal next door was gonna have a big say in directing its orbit!

WHAT A DISH!

*Spring a few surprises on your family this year —
here are four main dishes and four "puddings" — and each makes up a seasonal meal you can
put together simply and sensationally!*

Spring Surprise

HAM AND PASTA SALAD
(Ingredients for four throughout.)
225 g/8 oz. macaroni
350 g/12 oz. cooked ham, chopped
225 g/8 oz. Bel Paese cheese, chopped
4 celery stalks, chopped
5 spring onions, chopped
15 ml/1 tablespoonful mustard
225 ml/8 fl. oz. mayonnaise
Salt and pepper
2 hard-boiled eggs, chopped
2 tomatoes, cut into wedges

Method:
Cook macaroni in boiling, salted water for about 8 to 10 minutes, or until soft. Drain, then cool. Put ham, cheese, celery and spring onions into a salad bowl. Stir in the macaroni. Stir the mustard into the mayonnaise and season to taste. Stir into the salad and toss well to coat. Garnish with the chopped eggs and tomato wedges.

MANDARIN DREAM
1 x 450 g/1 lb. can mandarin oranges, drained
50 g/2 oz. flaked almonds
225 ml/8 fl. oz. sour cream
30 ml/2 tablespoonfuls chopped crystallised ginger

Method:
Mix the oranges, almonds and sour cream together. Sprinkle over the crystallised ginger and chill for 15 minutes.

Summer Sensation

TUNA STUFFED TOMATOES
4 large firm tomatoes, halved and de-seeded
2 hard-boiled eggs, finely chopped
1 x 200 g/7 oz. can tuna, drained and flaked
10 ml/2 teaspoonfuls capers
5 ml/1 teaspoonful chopped fresh parsley
45 ml/3 tablespoonfuls mayonnaise, Pepper,
4 stuffed olives, halved

Method:
Turn the tomato shells upside down to drain. Meanwhile, put all the remaining ingredients, except the olives, in a small bowl and mix well. Pile the mixture into the tomato shells and garnish with the olives.

STRAWBERRY WHIP DRINK
½ kg/1 lb. strawberries
900 ml/1½ pints milk
225 g/8 oz. ice-cream
50 g/2 oz. sugar
2.5 m/½ teaspoonful vanilla essence
Ice cubes
75 ml/3 fl. oz. double cream, whipped
4 whole strawberries to garnish

Method:
Rub strawberries through sieve into a bowl, beat in the milk, ice-cream, sugar and vanilla essence. Or alternatively, mix to a puree in a blender. Put some ice cubes into four tall glasses. Pour over the pureed mixture and top with a generous swirl of cream. Put a strawberry on the top of each glass.

Autumn Appetizers

CHILLI CON CARNE
30 ml/2 tablespoonfuls oil
1 large onion, chopped
2 garlic cloves, crushed
125 g/4 oz. bacon slices, chopped
½ kg/1 lb. minced beef
1 x 400 g/14 oz. can red kidney beans, drained
2 teaspoonfuls chilli powder
Salt

Method:
Heat the oil in a saucepan. Add the onion, garlic and bacon and fry for 5 minutes. Add the beef and fry for a further 5 minutes or until it loses its pinkness. Stir in the remaining ingredients. Cover and simmer for 1 hour.

BLACKCURRANT FLUMMERY
1 packet lemon jelly
300 ml/10 fl. oz. boiling water
60 ml/4 tablespoonfuls blackcurrant syrup
150 ml/5 fl. oz. evaporated milk
150 ml/5 fl. oz. plain yoghurt
8 slices crystallised lemon

Method:
Dissolve the jelly in the water, stirring constantly. Put aside until it begins to set. Divide between two bowls. Beat the milk into one and the yoghurt into the other. Spoon a little of each mixture into four serving glasses and chill until set. Decorate with the lemon slices.

Winter Warmers

TOAD IN THE HOLE
15 g/½ oz. butter
½ kg/1 lb. pork sausages

Batter:
125 g/4 oz. flour
Pinch of salt
1 egg
300 ml/10 fl. oz. milk

Method:
Sift flour and salt into a bowl. Beat in the egg and gradually add enough milk to form a stiff batter. Set aside for 10 minutes. Add the remaining milk, stirring constantly.

Melt the butter in a flameproof baking dish and add the sausages. Put the dish into the oven, heated to hot (220 deg. C., 425 deg. F., or Gas Mark 7) and cook for 10 minutes or until evenly browned. Pour over the batter, reduce the oven temperature to moderate (180 deg. C., 350 deg. F., or Gas Mark 4) and bake for 30 minutes or until the batter is golden brown and has risen.

CARAMEL BANANAS
50 g/2 oz. butter
150 g/5 oz. brown sugar
4 large bananas, sliced
50 ml/2 fl. oz. single cream
600 ml/1 pint vanilla ice-cream

Method:
Melt the butter in a frying pan. Add the sugar and stir until it has dissolved. Stir in the banana slices so that they are thoroughly coated. Cook for 5 minutes or until the bananas are tender. Stir in the cream. Divide the ice-cream between four glasses and spoon over the banana mixture.

TAKE TWO GIRLS...

We gave lucky readers, Lorna (15) and Lorraine (17), completely new model-girl images in our marvellous make-over! They really made the most of it, too — they took to those clicking cameras and glaring lights like true professionals! Didn't they do well?!

LORRAINE'S DAY FACE
1. Gold eyeshadow.
2. Darker mustard shade at outer corners.
3. Green frosted powder as eyeliner.
4. Ivory highlighter.
5. Caramel blusher.
6. Gold lipstick.

"Just what are they going to do with us...?

...but after a bit of a chat...

LORNA'S DAY FACE
1. Dusty blue eyeshadow.
2. Dark, deep blue shade on outer corners — darker skins can really show off dramatic colours!
3. Ivory highlighter.
4. Mixture of reddish and caramel blusher.
5. Bright red lipstick.

...we end up looking like this...

LORRAINE'S DAY OUTFIT
Khaki jacket and bag from
a selection at
Laurence Corner, 62-64
Hampstead Rd., London N11.
Green culottes from main
branches of Laura Ashley.
*Green sweatshirt,
pink braces and pink belt*
from Flip, Long Acre,
Curtain Rd. and Kings Rd.,
London. *Striped tights*
by Mary Quant, *horn
earrings* by Corocraft
and *headband* by Adrien
Mann, from selections at
most major department stores.

...and this!

LORNA'S DAY OUTFIT
Nautical jacket and trousers
by Zed from branches
of Top Shop and Chelsea Girl.
Jumper by Irvine Sellars
from branches of Mates.
Red belt by Salisburys from
branches. *Sailor hat*
from Laurence Corner,
as before. *Bracelets* by
Corocraft and *necklace*
by Adrien Mann, as before.

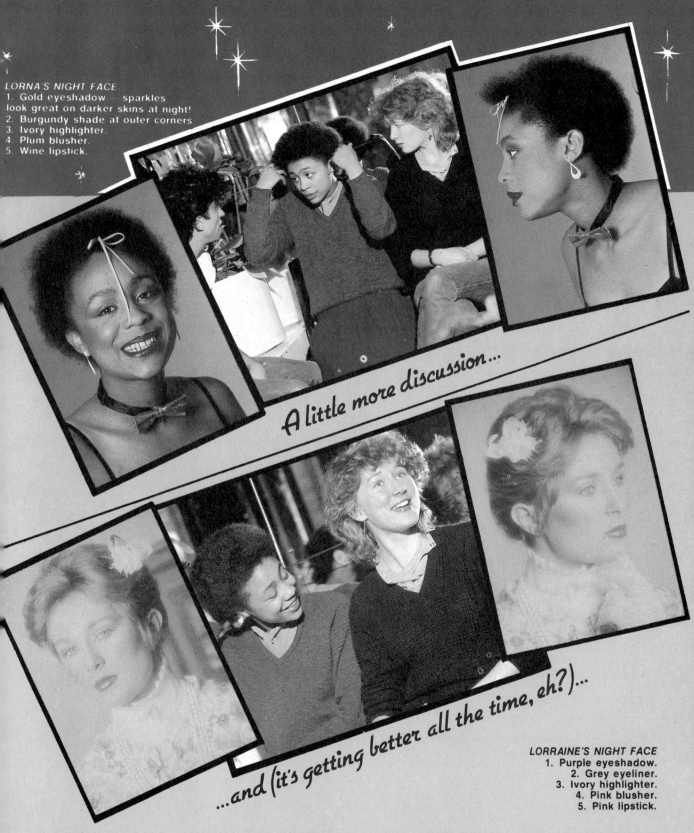

LORNA'S NIGHT FACE
1. Gold eyeshadow — sparkles look great on darker skins at night!
2. Burgundy shade at outer corners
3. Ivory highlighter.
4. Plum blusher.
5. Wine lipstick.

A little more discussion...

...and (it's getting better all the time, eh?)...

LORRAINE'S NIGHT FACE
1. Purple eyeshadow.
2. Grey eyeliner.
3. Ivory highlighter.
4. Pink blusher.
5. Pink lipstick.

NOTE THESE NOTES!
FOUNDATION: applied with a damp sponge, and always underneath lipstick to help it last longer.
FACE POWDER: applied with a wad of cotton wool, excess dusted off with a sable brush.
BLUSHER: applied in cheek hollows, dusted upwards and outwards; sometimes used on sides of forehead as shader.
HIGHLIGHTER: eyes — applied just under the browbone/eyebrow; face — along cheekbones, and sometimes on temples. Highlighter and blusher when used properly give more curves to the face, light shades emphasising features, darker ones giving more depth.
EYESHADOW: darker shades at the outer eye corners, helped give wide-apart, almond-shaped eyes.
MASCARA: applied in two or three sweeping black coats.
LIPSTICK: and lip pencil filled in the lips, with careful lipbrush outlines.
HAIR ASSISTANCE: by staff at Sissors, King's Rd., London.
MAKE-UP: by Anne Candy.

69

...we end up looking like this...

LORRAINE'S NIGHT OUTFIT
Dress, blouse and petticoats from Laura Ashley, as before. *White crochet gloves* by Dents, from all A & N Stores, Alders, Owen Owen and Dingles. *Pink earrings* and *pastel bracelets* by Corocraft, as before. *Pearls* by Marvella, from Harrods, Knightsbridge; Dickins & Jones, Regent St., London; Rackhams, Birmingham; and Kendles, Manchester.

...and this!
Thanks, Patches!..."

LORNA'S NIGHT OUTFIT
Rumba dress by Mister Ant
from Dickins & Jones,
Regent St., London;
Separate Fayre, 76
Ballards Lane, Finchley N3;
Mr Charles Ltd.,
Herringthorpe Valley Rd.,
Rotherham, Yorkshire;
and Viva, 113 Bradshaw Gate,
Lea, Lancs. *Gold bow-tie*
from Flip, as before.
Yellow earrings by
Corocraft, as before. *Yellow
ribbon and bracelets,*
model's own.

ALL IN A DREAM...

A Patches romantic short story by Barbara Jacobs.

I WOKE up before dawn with the dream again, shouting his name into the darkness, my hand outstretched, reaching for his hand. But my grip closed on emptiness, and when I opened my tear-filled eyes I was in my bedroom in a tangle of clean linen sheets and damask bedcovers.

"John!" I cried, but his name came echoing back at me from the high walls and the heavily-draped windows.

The dream was always the same. I was back at home, in the village, at the stile where my mother had left me all those years ago. But in the dream, I wasn't a child. I was me, now, grown into almost a woman, but tired and cold, as I'd been before I found this new home. I knew, even in the dream, that I was waiting for John to come home and take care of me. And he appeared, as I'd known he always would, over the brow of the hill, running, limping through the sharp frosty stubble, running towards me in his soldier's uniform, not dead at all, wonderfully alive . . .

"Just a dream," I reminded myself, wiping away the tears on the lace-edged cuff of my nightgown. But this time, something stopped me from snuggling back into the warmth to sleep again. My heart was beating too quickly for sleep, and there was a tightness in my stomach.

There had been something extra in my dream this time. This time he'd touched me, touched my face with his soft hand, not the cold clammy hand of a ghost, but a human hand, warm and tender, and he'd said, as he touched me, "I promised I'd be back. I knew you'd be here. I'm glad you got my message!"

I stretched my legs out of bed into the icy cold, shivering with fear and certainty. This dream, this time, had to be the message. John and I always

could read each other's minds. I had to go home. I had to leave this tall house in the tree-lined London square, and make my way back to the village where I'd left my heart.

Quietly I pulled open the heavy curtains, and peered out into the misty dusk of early morning. Across the square, a tall Christmas tree shimmered in its coat of frost. Christmas 1919. More than a year since the Great War ended, more than a year of waiting for my soldier to come home.

It was time for dreams to end. I'd decided. John's message couldn't be ignored. I dressed noiselessly, terrified that I'd wake Alice, my little maid, who slept lightly in the tiny room next to mine. She'd warned me often enough about living in the past. She tried to talk me out of silly ideas of loving a dead soldier, and did her best to encourage Michale Vaizey, who visited me too often for my comfort. I wasn't in love with Michale, wasn't prepared to play the part of his pampered wife, closed between the four walls of his elegant house in Chelsea. I'd refused to marry him four times already.

"Why not, Mary?" he'd begged me.

"Because I'm too young, and I love someone else," I told him every time, and every time he'd say:

"Eighteen's a good age for betrothal and John Weston's dead. Everyone knows that. Your father showed you the letter . . .!" He'd sigh, but I'd tell him I'd never believe John to be dead, until I saw his body in a dream, lying in a field of poppies, like the other dead soldiers, all those others.

"John speaks to me in dreams . . ." I wanted to tell him, but I never did. Somehow, I knew that Michale Vaizey wouldn't understand that, nor the fact that I wanted to lead a useful life, at the side

of the man I loved. John would train to be a doctor, when he came home, and I'd manage to persuade my father, somehow, to let me train as a nurse.

I'd helped at Whitelands, at the hospital they turned it into, three years before, worked from morning till dusk in the dirt and the despair, and then run home to Gran to tend her through the long hours of sickness, every single night, until her last.

I PACKED a small bag, just a nightgown, some stout shoes, some underclothing, and my souvenirs — old browned letters from John, from the early days before he was sent to the trenches.

He hadn't written since that day, more than eighteen months ago. Then I fastened round my neck the heavy gold locket that my father had given me. John's faded photograph was inside, and a lock of my dead mother's hair. Swallowing back tears and memories, I pulled on my heavy fur-lined street coat, and opened my bedroom door slowly.

I crept down the curving stairs, into the wide marble-floored hallway, and took one last look at the world I was leaving, the house that gleamed with mahogany and crystal, portraits in heavy gilt frames lining the sweep of the stairway, and on the first floor my father, sleeping behind brocade drapes, with his new wife, Elizabeth. I couldn't leave him without a word. Taking up the pen on the writing table in the hall, I scribbled a note, "Gone to Marston. Will return with John as soon as possible. Your loving daughter, Mary."

The tram-ride was as frightening as usual, a jolting ride in the frosty morning, packed between tired men, exhausted by a long war, returned to a country that was working hard to be a land fit

for heroes. But if the tram wasn't enough to make me wonder if I was doing the right thing, the station was.

I'd only been in a railway station once in my life, when Father brought me the year before from the country. Then the place had been full of returning soldiers, and I'd held my father's arm tightly, jumping at every whistle and hoot, shivering in the swirling steam and smoke, looking into every soldier's face to see whether one of them was John. Now, alone, I was petrified.

I managed to find the ticket office, and bought one for Marston. I was confused by the instructions for changing trains and my head was whirling with the noise, the screaming and shouting, the heavy clanging and hissing of the steaming trains. I ran through acrid smoke, to the barrier that the ticket-seller directed me to.

"Marston. Third class? Rear of train. Change at King's Lynn and Wroxall Junction," the man at the barrier snapped at me.

I finally managed to find a seat, right at the end of the train, and squeezed myself between an old man, wheezing and puffing, and a young girl, about my age, with rouged red cheeks and piled-up red hair, who stared at me sullenly. When the train pulled out, hissing and juddering, the girl was still staring. A young man put my bag on the rack for me, and the girl still stared.

The train rattled with a rapid clickety-click sound, and the grimy outskirts of London flashed past the windows.

The others had lost interest in me by now. The young man in the corner had brought out a mouth organ and started to play some of the war songs, and the girl with the red cheeks and the staring eyes began to sing in a raucous voice, "It's A Long Way To Tipperary." Soon everyone had joined in.

Except me. I sat pretending to sleep, hiding my tears, remembering John singing that very song to me, just before he left . . .

M Y earliest memories were of my mother, and John, but first of my mother, a pale sad lady with huge dark eyes, walking me for days through wintry countryside, coughing, never complaining, telling me that soon I'd be warm, soon . . .

I must have been four years old, tiny enough to take refuge in tears, tiny enough to stop crying when my mum said that I had to stop, tiny enough to trust her completely, even when, after four days long, exhausting walk, without food, with hardly any rest, she'd brought me to the edge of Marston, and sat me on the stile past the drive to Whitelands.

"Stay here, Mary," she'd said. "Stay here, until someone comes along. Then say that Mummy's ill, and you're all alone. Someone will take care of you. I had friends here, once!"

I hardly understood, only that I was to stay there, and that my mother was going somewhere. I remember holding her tightly, begging her not to go. I remember her tears as she walked away. And then, the loneliness of the long day, waiting, cold and lonely, shivering in my thin print dress.

John found me. He must have been six or seven at the time, but gentle, even then. He was the one who heard my story, and went to fetch his father, Dr Weston, and a crowd of curious villagers. They'd already found my mother. Her body had floated down river into the centre of the village. They knew her, all right.

"Hetty Baker was never any good!" I heard someone say.

"Never knew about the child, though!"

"So that's why she left so suddenly! Well, well!"

They stood staring at me, vicious, hostile. I was four years old, and trying to grapple with the knowledge that my mother was never coming back. Never. Tears trickled down my cheeks. John ran across, and put his arms round my shoulders, and Dr Weston followed him.

"Careful, John. Her mother had consumption — only had a week or so to live, anyway. Perhaps the little girl has it, too. I'd better examine her." He approached me, an older version of the little boy whose big blue eyes still looked into mine with compassion and perhaps, even then, love.

And just as the doctor reached me, put out his hand for me to take, a woman pushed through the crowd.

"What's all this then?" she asked, elbowing her way through. "You've nothing better to do than stand and jeer at a poor little mite who's all alone in the world and doesn't understand a word of what you're saying. Maybe it's just as well! Here, doctor. I'll carry the child, poor love." And with that she swept me into her warm plump arms, and I lay cradled against the smell of baking. She always smelled like new loaves, and told me I was to call her Gran.

I loved her then and there.

"Anyone saying a word against Hetty Baker, or Hetty Baker's child, has me to contend with now. Hetty, God rest her soul, was no worse than any of you, and better than some! I'll have you remember that. And this little girl's looked after by me, from now on!"

And so it was. I grew up happy in Gran's love, and the unanswered questions about my background didn't seem to worry her. Of course they didn't. She knew exactly who I was. But I didn't find that out until after she'd died, too.

They were golden years for me. I went to school, when I'd recovered from the consumption, and learned to write, and read a little, and count my numbers, and sew, and learn about country things — flights of birds, spring flowers, sheep and cattle, and hero-worship. Everyone loved John Weston, the doctor's son, with his soft low voice, his cornflower eyes.

I was more spellbound by his kindness than anyone. Somewhere in the darkness of almost forgotten memory, I believed that he had saved my life. I followed him from school, listened to his stories, walked behind him like a faithful puppy when he strode away on fishing trips, and pined half to death when he went away to big school.

He was eleven then, and I was nine, almost ready to leave school myself and start "in service" at the big house, Whitelands, where Lord and Lady Banville lived, an eccentric hard-drinking couple, very rarely seen by the villagers, since their only son had left home and disappeared ten years before.

Gran arranged the job for me. We needed the money. I was to be housemaid, living in the big house when the Banvilles were in the village, returning to Gran's when they left, each winter, for their London home.

I didn't much like the job, but I was glad to have some way of helping Gran out. And the summers were easy, when the Banvilles left. Then we'd keep the house clean and aired, polish the furniture, but much of the time was ours, to do what we wished. I searched out John Weston.

HE changed in those years before the war, changed from a boy into a serious young man with just a hint of laughter in his blue eyes.

He was worried about his father. Some days, when I'd find him, and creep up silently as he sat fishing, or reading by the river, he'd start talking as if to no-one in particular, but to me, really, about the future, about his plans to be a doctor, like his father.

"But he's ill, Mary. Maybe he won't live to see me into university.

I'd slide to his side, and touch his hand, gently, as if to tell him that I knew what being alone meant, and he always knew what I meant by that touch, and always turned his hazy blue eyes towards me, and smiled.

I'd fallen in love with him by this time. But I said and did nothing for two years, until he came home, finally, for his father's funeral. That day, he kissed me.

I found him alone and crying by the graveside one day. I held him in my arms, put his head on my shoulder and talked to him about fear and loneliness. By then, the whole world knew all about fear and loneliness. Almost all the village men, and half the village boys, were fighting in the trenches.

Whitelands had fallen into decay for a year or two. Lord and Lady Banville had sailed to America to be reunited with their long-lost son, and their house was to be turned into a hospital.

Gran said I'd probably find work there, and that's what I wanted to do, instead of sitting hour after hour, sewing shirts for the soldiers who were dying. Gran always plucked a hair out of her own head, and sewed it into the final seam of the shirt. "For luck," she said.

But there didn't seem to be much luck around, anywhere. On that warm summer day, John and I talked, huddled together, about a future that would never come.

"I have to leave. They've called me up, Mary. I'm going into the Medical Corps at the end of the summer," he whispered, holding me.

"You'll be back. Gran said you'll be back. She knows about these things. The war's nearly over," I told him.

And he turned to me, so slowly, his face pale in sunshine.

"Will you wait for me, Mary?" he asked, his lips closing on mine.

"For ever," I whispered, then the world spun like a whipped top, round and round, silver, and cornflower blue, like his eyes.

For ever had taken me through the long hot summer when we cycled through flower-edged lanes and chased along empty beaches, and talked, and kissed again and again.

It had taken me through the agonies of that terrible goodbye.

It had taken me through the empty months without a letter after the one saying that he'd been posted to the front line.

It had taken me through Gran's death, the end of the war, and the news that John was missing ''presumed dead.'' But ''for ever'' is stronger than ''presumed dead.'' It goes through agonies of waiting.

After Gran died, the hospital closed, and the village was different. I lived from day to day in Gran's house, wondering how I'd manage to survive without a soul in the world. And then, from out of nowhere, my father arrived. His name was Lord Banville.

Not the old Lord, of course. *He'd* died in America. My father was the son who'd broken the old man, by running away with Hetty Baker, the housemaid, and marrying her, and leaving her to manage alone, with me. My mother had sewn my birth certificate into the rags I wore on that long journey, and Gran had found it, and said nothing. She'd known what my mother had wanted for me, to be brought up like a country girl, as she'd been brought up. But at the end, Gran had written to America, asking my father to collect me.

He'd come, half out of his mind with guilt and grief to claim me, and he'd taken me, with Elizabeth, his new wife, to live in London, to wealth and luxury . . .

KING'S LYNN!'' someone shouted, and the train jolted to a halt.

''King's Lynn!'' I gasped, grabbing for my bag, pulling my coat round me, lurching through the open door on the crowded, smoky platform.

But when I opened my bag it was empty. No ticket, no money, no change of clothes. Just the letters from John in the inside pocket, tucked well down. Someone in that crowded compartment had stolen everything I had, except hope.

I still had that. I managed to explain to the man at the ticket barrier what had happened, and unbelievably, he took my word, and let me walk through, into the seedy streets of the town. Perhaps it was the richness of my dress that convinced him that I was telling the truth.

''Marston?'' he said, scratching his head, pointing down the streets. ''West of here, that is. About fifty miles. There's a bus to Langley, and then . . . by then it'll be nightfall. Haven't you any relatives you could contact?''

''Relatives! Oh yes! Yes, I'll do that!'' I smiled, swallowing hard. I didn't want my father to come after me, believing me to be completely mad. I knew he'd been worried about my belief in my dreams for a long time. I'd manage without him. Somehow.

I found the pawn shop easily enough. The man behind the desk offered me pennies for my bag, only a few shillings for my coat, and a few more for the lace, and the decorative buttons on my dress. Then his eyes gleamed as he reached for my locket.

''No!'' I gasped, pushing it down inside my dress. ''I'd rather starve than . . .'' Than part with the mementos of my mother and John.

But starving looked likely. The serge dress was warm enough indoors, or under my thick coat, but too thin to withstand the biting East wind. And I was hungry. I'd left home without breakfast, with just a wild idea in my head, nothing in my stomach. The wild idea had kept me going so far. Now, as I paid my bus fare, and looked at the pennies left in my hand to sustain me through twenty more miles of muddy country, in mid December, I wondered if perhaps I'd believed in ghosts for too long.

I TRIED to sleep on the bus, but when I did, just for an hour, I saw John again, trudging through mud, limping across stubble fields, calling my name so plaintively, that I awoke crying. It was dark and bitterly cold.

''Langley. Last stop,'' the conductor shouted. I was the only passenger left. Aching with cold and hunger, I climbed out, into a star-filled night.

There was an inn in Langley, but I knew that I, a stranger, daren't call in at night. Country folk don't like women alone walking into their inns. When my mother and I had walked, all those years ago . . .

The flash of memory came blindingly. I'd forgotten that time, that long walk, but now I remembered, trudging through the cold and darkness, like this, creeping into barns for warmth and shelter among the hay . . .

I walked for miles, my teeth chattering, my hands and feet numb, before I found a barn. There, in the sweet-smelling pile of hay, I made a bed, and slept until dawn.

The day dawned clear and bright with frost. I took out the pennies from my pocket, shook myself clean of hay, and walked through frozen mud to the farmhouse, where I managed to buy a jug of milk and some bread, paying all my money to avoid questions from the suspicious farmer's wife.

And then I started walking again, the roads familiar now. The sun rose higher in the sky as I walked, warm enough to turn the hard lanes to mud again, but not warm enough to penetrate the coldness that numbed every bone in my body. By the time Marston church spire appeared on the pale horizon, I knew that I was beaten.

My shoes, dainty London shoes, had broken. One heel had been torn off on a stile. The other had split at the toes. Each step was an agony of pain. I was too ill, too tired to walk any further for silly dreams. Hot tears ran down my cold cheeks, and I threw away my shoes, striking out, slowly, painfully, towards the church in the distance. I had to reach it. I had to reach Marston. Someone there would contact my father for me, give me a hot bath and hot food while I waited for him to arrive, and I'd go home quietly, knowing that there would be no more dreams.

I had to admit defeat. John was dead. No running away into the cold and darkness I'd once known would bring him back to me. I'd lived in dreams too long. It was time to be sensible, to forget the past, and live in a comfortable future.

I dragged myself across the fields until I could walk no more. The sun was setting, red, and beautiful, and angry. I dropped to my knees, clinging to the stile over the field road, the stile where my mother had left me all those years ago. My dress, torn and muddy, hung in shreds. I wanted to sleep and forget. I wanted . . .

''Mary! You got my message! You came!'' the voice echoed, from my dream.

I shook my head. ''No more dreams, please!'' I cried. ''No more. Leave me alone!''

''Mary!''

I looked up into the sunset. John stood on the brow of the hill, and then he ran, limping, towards me through the frosty stubble.

''Mary!''

A hand reached out to touch my face. It was soft, not the cold clammy hand of a ghost, but a human hand, warm and tender.

''I promised I'd be back. I knew you'd be here. I'm glad you got my message,'' he said, placing his hand under my chin, lifting my face to look into his face.

His eyes were deep cornflower blue as ever. The jagged line of a scar ran from the corner of his mouth down his neck, under the collar of his officer's jacket.

''I've been in hospital, in France, miles from anywhere. I never thought I'd get back . . .''

''John!'' I breathed, touching him, warily, the way you touch a dream, with the tips of your fingers. And then my arms circled him, and he clasped me tight, bringing warmth and life back into my body, the way he always had done. He'd never stopped caring.

''I'll take care of you, Mary. We'll be all right now,'' he whispered, touching my lips with his kiss.

''For ever,'' I whispered, knowing that this time for ever would mean for the rest of our lives ★

FOOD, GLORIOUS

A balanced diet is essential to good health *and* looking

YOU can't drive an engine without the right kind of fuel and you can't expect your body to work well without proper food, either!

Your diet is important and you should aim for a good balance in your eating habits as soon as you possibly can. It's no use eating nothing but chips and chocolate — your system will soon rebel! You'll start feeling tired and lethargic; your skin will become dull and your hair *won't* be your crowning glory!

If you're looking and feeling grotty, right now, then you need to take extra care and improve your food intake right away . . .

Things To Avoid

Our way of life has altered drastically over the years and this is reflected in our food.

Processing has now become an everyday occurrence with canning, freezing and instant preparations, which all go towards taking the goodness out of food.

Refining has also taken over to a great extent, although this process has started to reverse. We have been eating so much refined sugar and flour that our health is being badly affected by it. This refining process removes a lot of the natural vitamins food contains and just fills us with stodge.

That's why it's such a good idea to eat fresh rather than frozen, natural rather than refined — it all adds up to the way you look and feel in the end!

Go Nuts!

Past beliefs concentrated on protein as being the most important part of our diet, especially in meat, poultry and dairy products.

However, you should now try to get as much protein as possible from other things, too — grains, nuts and seeds, for instance. Try not to rely solely on animal protein as this could be harmful.

A really healthy diet is based on grains/nuts/seeds, vegetables and fruit. Don't forget dairy products completely, though; supplement your diet with milk and other dairy products, vegetable oils and honey,

FOOD!

good, so start weighing up the situation . . . . now!

cutting out so much meat and poultry.

What An Appetite!

These days food is plentiful for most people and many people eat purely for the sake of it.

A large percentage of the population grossly over-eat, with the result that they become overweight and decidely unhealthy. If *you* don't want to end up unfit and fat, the rule here is to eat only when you're hungry. Ask for a smaller plate, which means smaller portions. It isn't good to eat huge meals each day–you're better with several small meals.

The Whole Food

Try to eat as much fresh, wholesome food as possible.

Raw food is especially good for you because none of the goodness has been "cooked" out of it.

Wholewheat and wholemeal breads not only taste delicious but also give you much needed roughage. Bran sprinkled over your food is also very good for you. Don't ignore potatoes — baked potatoes are full of goodness and the skin is especially nutritious.

All these foods are very filling, too, so you don't need to eat as much of them.

Frying Tonight

Frying isn't particularly good for the food and certainly isn't beneficial to yourself!

You'd be amazed at the amount of fat that comes out of food when it's heated, so imagine how much will be in it if you fry that food!

There are plenty of far better, healthier cooking methods — baking, poaching, grilling, boiling, to name but a few. If you're continually eating fried food, your hair and skin will soon be looking pretty unhealthy. So try to steer clear of that frying pan as much as possible.

The Raw Truth

It's quite a good idea to have one day a week when you eat just raw foods. OK, so this doesn't sound too tempting but you'll be surprised.

When you cook vegetables you lose some of the goodness and the longer you cook the more you lose! Raw vegetables and fruit can make a lovely, colourful and tasty meal. Grate some raw carrot and have tomatoes, lettuce, pieces of apple and pear, add a hunk of cheese and some nuts. That's a very filling meal especially if you have some wholemeal bread and relishes. With a little bit of thought you can *really* enjoy your food and benefit from it!

Drink Up!

Fizzy drinks might look colourful and refreshing but you'd be better to avoid them as much as possible.

They're full of sugar and don't really quench your thirst. Try to drink as much water as possible. The more water you drink, the better your skin will be and the more your eyes will sparkle.

Instead of reaching for the lemonade bottle, buy fresh orange or other fruit drinks. They don't have sugar added and taste wonderful! In fact, if you drink fresh orange juice with your meals you can double your intake of iron, which is especially important to teenage girls.

Remember, if you eat only the best, your body will repay you by being fit and healthy. Eat well and you'll look — and feel *great*!

MAKING

Scrape your hair back, draw up a chair and sit down make-up-less in front of a mirror. Now you can start from scratch, shaping and shading your face shape into something sensational. Here's how!

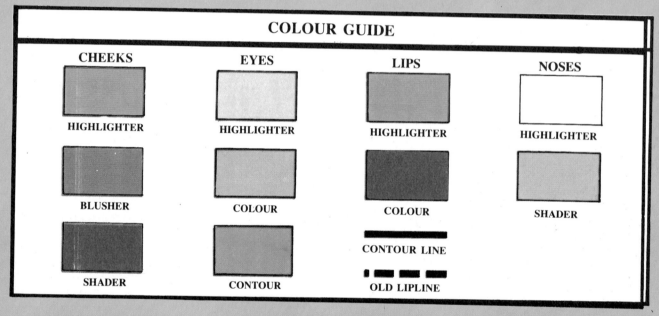

COLOUR GUIDE

CHEEKS
- HIGHLIGHTER
- BLUSHER
- SHADER

EYES
- HIGHLIGHTER
- COLOUR
- CONTOUR

LIPS
- HIGHLIGHTER
- COLOUR
- CONTOUR LINE
- OLD LIPLINE

NOSES
- HIGHLIGHTER
- SHADER

FACES *Face facts are easy if you remember these basic rules: darken shades play down areas of the face; light, highlighting shades emphasise and bring forward features. Remember to use a complete cosmetic brush kit – eyebrow brush and comb, eye-shadow sponge applicator, eyeshadow brush, eyeliner brush, lip brush and complexion brush – and you're ready to face up to things that aren't quite perfect!*

Round: highlight cheekbones and apply blusher to the hollows of cheeks. Use darker shader below blusher and along jawbone to play down roundness.

Heart: highlight cheekbones and apply blusher below. Use darker shade at sides of forehead and on temples to play down width of forehead.

Square: again highlight cheekbones and apply blusher below. But put darker shader at the corner of the face to play down the squareness.

FACES!

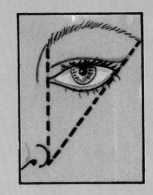

EYES *When shaping eyes, remember your eyebrows! They should begin just above the inner corner of the eye and finish just beyond the outer corner (see illus.).*

Oval: highlight actual cheekbones. Apply blusher under cheekbones and a slightly darker shade just below that to emphasise cheekbones.

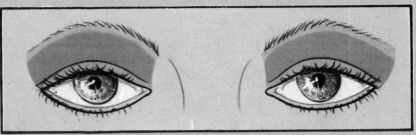

Deep Set: apply pale colour to whole of lower lid. Use a dark, plain colour to contour above socket and then highlight just below browbone.

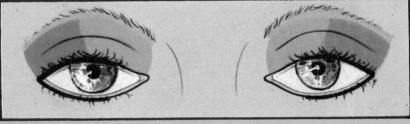

Prominent: use plain colour on inner side of eyelid and brow and a darker contour on outer side. Highlight just under browbone and apply eyeliner on the outer three-quarters of top and bottom lids and just above bottom lashes.

Long: highlight cheekbones and temples to widen the face. Apply blusher under cheekbones, and use a darker shade under chin and at top of forehead to play down length.

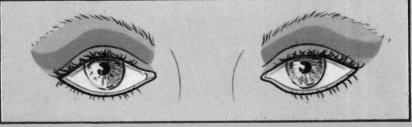

Small: apply pale colour on eyelid and darker contour on brow. Put highlighter just below eyebrow. (The space between eyebrow and lid will determine the height to which contour should be taken).

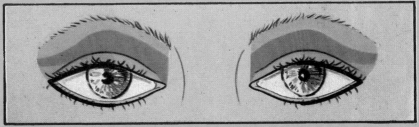

Close Set: widen them by applying high-lighter at the inner side of the lid and just under browbone (this opens small eyes up too). Apply colour on the outer edge of lid and contour above the socket line. Eyeliner should be applied on the outer edges of top and bottom lid, close to the lashes and just above the bottom lashes.

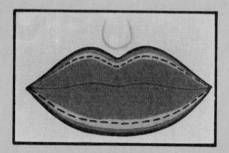

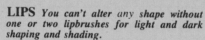

LIPS

You can't alter any shape without one or two lipbrushes for light and dark shaping and shading.

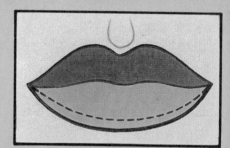

Thin: outline with a contour slightly outside your natural lip line (see lip key) without changing the actual lip shape. Fill in with colour and highlight over your natural lip line so it blends into the new contour line and creates fullness.

Thick: do the reverse here — trace a a new contour inside the natural lip line. Fill in with a plain colour, not frosted — remember, pale shades emphasise features.

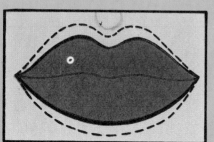

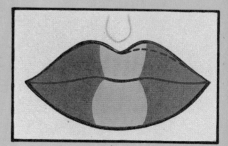

Thin Upper Lip: outline with a contour until it balances lower lip. Fill in with colour. Use a frosted highlighter over lipstick on upper lip to bring it forward.

Thin Lower Lip: contour outside the natural line of the lower lip. Use a frosted highlighter on the lower lip, over your colour.

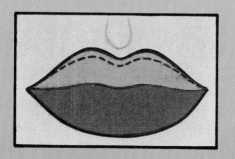

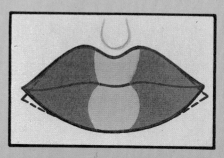

Uneven: add to the narrow side with a contour outline, to help balance the lip shape. Fill in with colour. Apply highlighter in centre of lips for an even, central fullness.

Down-Turned: outline a contour curve from the centre of the lower lip to the corners and fill in with lip colour. Draw an upward curve at the corner of the top lip to pull it upwards, and fill in also.

NOSES *A general tip – plucking out the hair between the eyebrows can often make your nose less pronounced.*

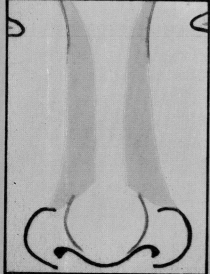

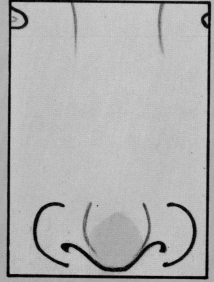

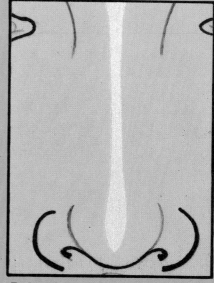

To Slim A Broad Nose: blend darker foundation all the way down either side, fading out at the tip.

To Shorten A Long Nose: apply dark foundation to the nose tip.

To Lengthen And Narrow A Nose: apply highlighter down the bridge.

Search For A Star

Kristen, Cheryl and Sandra were the best of friends . . .

DID YOU SEE ADAM ANT ON " TOP OF THE POPS " LAST NIGHT?

YEAH. HE'S FANTASTIC.

But Sandra could go one better in her dreams!

OF COURSE, THE TELLY DOESN'T REALLY DO ADAM JUSTICE. HE'S MUCH BETTER-LOOKING IN REAL LIFE.

OH? YOU KNOW HIM THEN, DO YOU?

C'MON THEN, SANDRA, TELL US! WHEN DID YOU MEET ADAM? WE'RE DYING TO KNOW, AREN'T WE, KRISTEN?

OH, YEAH . . . I CAN HARDLY WAIT!

IT WAS LAST WEEK ACTUALLY . . . AT THE MAKE-UP COUNTER IN ONE OF THE SHOPS IN TOWN.

Continued on page 84

WE'RE GONNA MAKE YOU A ST★R

So you want to be a star? You want to sing, dance, act! But do you have what it takes to follow that twisting, turning road to fame and fortune? Grab a dice and a couple of counters, and we can find out right now . . .

20. Working as a part-time waitress, you spill boiling soup in a man's lap. He offers you a recording contract if you promise not to do it again. Hurry ahead 5 squares.

19

18. Your very first mini-tour of Britain is cancelled because the No. 57 bus doesn't show up. Go back 5 squares.

 **17**

21. You are offered a guest spot on "Blankety Blank" or "Punchlines." This could ruin your career. Go back to the beginning!!

22

23. Your first big photo session, and the worst pea-soup fog since 1937 descends. Go back 4 squares.

16

26. Your first single goes to No. 1 in the Paraguay Top Ten. Big Deal. But move on 1 square anyway.

25

24. Your manager decides you ought to change your name. Wisely, though, you are not too keen on calling yourself Adam Ant. Move ahead 3 squares.

31. Overhearing you and a friend gossiping, Andrew Lloyd Webber offers you a part in the film version of "Cats." Move ahead 1 square.

28. You are a wow on "Top Of The Pops"! Jimmy Savile's cigar burns through the straps of your dress, and WOW! Move ahead 4 squares.

27

29. You audition for 600 stage musicals, then finally get the part of a young girl who has a nervous breakdown at an audition. Shiver and shake your way ahead 3 squares.

 **30**

YOU'RE A★ST★R

49. At last! You've made it! Now you know you must be a star! Patches have just printed your pin-up! Leap ahead 1 square and . . .

48. Bad luck! Just as you were doing so well, someone tears the last page out of Eamonn Andrews' big red book, so we'll never know how your story finishes. Go back to the beginning.

START HERE →

1.

2. You always enjoyed doing your party pieces at family get-togethers. Move on 3 squares.

3.

7. A passer-by hears you singing in the bath and offers to be your manager. He also offers to scrub your back, but skip that and move ahead 2 squares.

6

5

4. As a kid, you were thrown out of the school choir for doing a punk version of "Away In A Manger." Go back 3 squares.

8. You win a talent competition at a holiday camp. First prize is some talent. Take it and move on 5 squares.

9

10

11. Slightly better known, now, you are interviewed by "Patches," "The Gossip," "The Daily Blab," "The Music Magic" and "The Dandy"!! Move ahead 2 squares.

15. Showing great courage, you leave the Barbara Woodhouse School of Acting And Dancing to "make it on your own!" Move ahead 4 squares.

14. Your new manager throws a party to launch your career. Someone tries to break a bottle of champagne over your head. Dodge your way on 2 squares.

13

12. Your first gig is Cabaret Spot in a Car Wash. Squelch your way back 6 squares.

32

33. The first night of your musical, and you lose your voice. Go back to Square 22 and try to borrow your mum's voice for the evening.

34. A director hires you to sing the love theme from his latest film, "The Blood Feast Of The Man-Eating Chickens!" Move quickly ahead 2 squares.

35. You appear on "Swap Shop." But because of a mix-up, you are swapped for a teddy bear. This is definitely a set-back. Go back to Square 16.

39

38. Your first, sell-out concert. The audience scream and scream and scream! Because the theatre is on fire! Run for it, back 6 squares!

37. Your latest album goes platinum. Which is appropriate, 'cos now it matches your latest hair colour. Move ahead 2 squares.

36

40. You're nervous, and your first screen kiss lands somewhere around the leading man's left nostril. Go back to Square 30.

41. The Hollywood Oscar Ceremony. You are a hit, despite opening the wrong envelope and reading your granny's latest letter. Move ahead 1 square.

42

43. You are insulted, ridiculed, appear in a lousy play, and don't get paid. But you're on "The Morecambe and Wise Show," so all this is normal. Move ahead 2 squares.

47. You are plagued by doubts. Can you ever be a big star, if Janet Brown and Pamela Stephenson never ever impersonate you? Go back 5 squares.

46. You fall down the stairs on the Michael Parkinson show and land on the orchestra. Go back 4 squares.

45

44. A pillar-box follows you down the road, mumbling, "This Is Your Life . . . This Is Your Life . . ." Move ahead 1 square.

Continued from page 81

Continued on page 88

How Practical Are YOU?

Are you the type of person who could teach a scatter-brain a lesson in how to be practical? Or are you the kind who lumbers through life scattering bits of brain everywhere? Try our fun quiz and find out . . .

1. You're already late for a very important interview. The bus you're waiting for is even later. It starts to pour with rain and you don't have a coat. Do you . . .

c. panic and try to hitch a lift,

a. go to the nearest phone and call a taxi,

b. start running — you've got to get there somehow?

2. You're alone in the house and it's getting dark. Suddenly, all the lights go out. Do you . . .

a. light a match and make for the main fuse box,

b. lock yourself in your room and burst into tears,

c. go to find your next-door neighbour, but forget to take your keys and lock yourself out?

3. Your mum's ill and you have to take over the family cooking. Do you . . .

b. open every tin and frozen packet you can find,

c. stick with the one dish you can do well — and give 'em bacon butties for breakfast, dinner and tea,

a. shop carefully for dishes you *know* you can make because you have in the past?

4. You're baby-sitting, when the baby wakes up and yells, *very* loudly. Do you . . .

c. leave it for a bit and hope it'll go to sleep again,

a. give it a drink and try to calm it down by making ridiculous gooh-gah noises,

b. promptly ring the phone number you have for its parents?

5. You've borrowed a dress from your sister but accidentally spill orange juice all down the front. Do you . . .

b. hide it at the back of her wardrobe and hope she won't notice it's changed colour a bit,

c. shove it in the cleaner's right away, and "forget" to tell her,

a. make sure you get the mark out before she sees it?

6. You witness a small crime taking place. When the police question you, do you . . .

a. manage to sit down and give them a full description of the criminal,

b. tell them you're not at all sure what you saw, it all happened so fast,

c. manage to describe one or two things that did stick in your mind (like his wooden leg or false ears)?

7. The family cat goes missing. Do you . . .

c. shout yourself hoarse all day, calling its name,

a. search all over, get the neighbours' help and advertise in the local paper,

b. assume it'll come home — it was out for almost a week once?

8. Your boyfriend has managed to get tickets for a big concert. On the day, he gets flu and has to stay in bed. Do you . . .

a. sell them to the highest bidder, and make a tidy profit,

b. forget about everything except that your poor guy's got flu,

c. ask him if he'd mind if you gave his ticket to your best friend, and go along with her?

9. You go to have your hair cut, but the stylist chops it off far too short. Do you . . .

b. refuse to go out anywhere until it grows again,

a. have it dyed bright pink (in for a penny, in for a pound!),

c. burst into tears but console yourself with the thought

that it *will* grow — eventually?

10. You've been to visit a relative. The train you come home on is held up for two hours. Do you . . .

a. organise a sing-song in your carriage, and be the life and soul of the party,

c. manage to strike up a conversation with the people around you,

b. stare at the sheep out of the window, and wish you'd brought a book to read?

Now add up your score — mostly a, b or c — and turn to the conclusions to find out just how practical *you* are . . .

CONCLUSIONS

MOSTLY A:
Phew! You're *so* practical it hurts! Don't you *ever* get anything wrong? You're a very level-headed, down-to-earth and matter-of-fact sort of person. But while this is good in a way, some people may think you're a bit cold and unfeeling. You organise yourself and your entire life a bit like a computer programme, which is fine if you're a computer — but as you're a girl, maybe you ought to let your hair down occasionally, because if you don't, you might be missing out on an awful lot of fun!

MOSTLY B:
Ahem, d'you even know what the word "practical" means? You seem to be in a complete state of chaos all the time, and in any kind of unfamiliar situation you simply panic! You tend to hate any kind of responsibility because it makes you feel self-conscious and awkward. What you really need is somebody to keep an eye on you, because underneath all these flutterings is a really nice, sensitive person — you!

MOSTLY C:
You *do* have a practical streak which surfaces occasionally, but some of the time it does tend to get a bit lost! When you actually stop and think, you can cope with most situations perfectly well. Unfortunately, you frequently rush into things without thinking too clearly — and that's when your problems start!

87

Continued from page 85

THAT SEEMED TO GO FINE!

I CAN'T WAIT TO HEAR WHAT SANDRA TELLS US ABOUT THIS!

Next day . . .

WE WERE THINKING OF GOING SWIMMING ON SATURDAY AFTERNOON, SANDRA . . . DO YOU FANCY COMING?

ER—NO . . . I'LL BE BUSY ON SATURDAY AFTERNOON . . .

The day after . . .

THAT'S EXPENSIVE PERFUME YOU'VE BOUGHT, SANDRA? WHO ARE YOU TRYING TO IMPRESS?

ER—NO-ONE, I JUST THOUGHT I'D TRY SOMETHING NEW . . .

And on Saturday . . .

ARE YOU COMING TO WATCH THE FUN AS WELL, DANNY?

YOU BET. I WOULDN'T MISS IT!

THERE SHE IS . . . WAITING FOR CHEGGERS!

SHE ACTUALLY BELIEVES HE'S GOING TO SHOW UP!

Sandra waited . . . and waited . . .

SHE'S BEEN WAITING THREE-QUARTERS OF AN HOUR. DO YOU THINK SHE'S LEARNED HER LESSON?

YEAH. LET'S PUT HER OUT OF HER MISERY AND TELL HER IT WAS ALL A JOKE.

Then . . .

WAIT A MINUTE. THAT BOY'S GONE OVER TO TALK TO HER.

HEY, THAT'S MICK FOWLER. HE SINGS WITH A LOCAL GROUP. THEY'RE GREAT!

I WONDER WHAT THEY'RE TALKING ABOUT . . . ?

WHERE ARE THEY GOING?

I DON'T KNOW, BUT THINGS DON'T EXACTLY SEEM TO HAVE WORKED OUT THE WAY WE PLANNED!

Pop The...

If you're anything like this lot in the Patches office, you'... leap at the chance of a free night out with *anybody*! ... course, if it happened to be someone like Phil Oakey, Davi... Van Day, Midge Ure or Chas Smash, so much the better! B... which of these famous four would you choose as you... partner for a night on the town, and what does your choic... reveal about you? Just answer the simple questions in ou... star-studded quiz and you'll find out!

1. You're asked over to his place for a coffee. What's it like inside?
- a. Very, very smart — almost as though it had been made for looking at rather than living in.
- b. Functional, but not very homely, as he doesn't think of it as a permanent base.
- c. An absolute shambles with socks under the sofa, and half-full coffee cups all over the place!
- d. Quite small and neat, but friendly and homely, too.

2. Whereabouts d'you see him living?
- a. In a leafy, tree-lined avenue.
- d. In a fairly stylish flat above a shop in a suburban area of a large town.
- b. In a homely, northern town.
- c. In the area he was brought up in.

3. The two of you set off for an evening out. How do you travel?
- d. By taxi.
- b. On the bus — or by foot if it's not too far.
- a. In a specially-hired chauffeur-driven limousine.
- c. On the back of his trust... old scooter!

4. You've left it up to him to decide where you should go... How d'you think you'll b... spending the evening?
- c. Having fun with hi... mates.
- b. Watching an unusual film... at a cinema club.
- d. At an exclusive and ver... fashionable club wher... you go to be seen rathe... than to see.
- a. Dancing the night awa... at a very classy disco.

5. No matter where you... mystery boyfriend was takin... you, how would he dress?
- a. In smart, but casua... designer clothes.
- b. Dramatically — usuall... all in black or all in white...
- c. In comfortable jeans an... sweatshirt.

CONCLUSIONS

Mainly a's:
You really go for the boy-next-door type, don't you? You're a real down-to-earth soul, honest and unpretentious, and you choose your friends — both male and female — for these same qualities. You have never felt awkward with guys, and your boyfriends are always real mates. You probably muck around in no-nonsense clothes, yet you still look pretty country girl way — even if you live in the city! You don't like going places where you have to dress up and stand on ceremony as this makes you feel awkward. You get on well with your boyfriend's mates, and if you do come to the parting of the ways, you know you'll always have a firm shoulder to cry on if ever you should need one.

Chas Smash of Madness is just the man for you. As well as being crazy, he is a very honest person, whose fame and fortune haven't changed him one bit. He still lives in London's Camden Town, where he was brought up, and still keeps all his friends of many years ago.

He eats in friendly cafés rather than posh hotels and restaurants and still goes to the same old barber rather than a trendy hairdressing salon. But he isn't nutty all the time — there's a quiet, very intelligent side to him and he really appreciates a true friend.

Mainly d's:
You want everything on a plate, don't you? You want the sophistication of David Van Day, the very individual style of Phil Oakey, the friendly character of Chas Smash *and* the good looks of our fourth mystery man, all rolled into one! You set very high standards when it comes to boyfriends and you'd rather go without than settle for anyone less than perfect.

You want a guy with a sense of humour but he has to be suave and subtle as well. Your guy must have good dress sense but you'd rather...

...see him in a stylish suit than in anything too outrageous.

You also choose your boyfriend because of his circle of friends — they have to be as attractive as he is. *Midge Ure of Ultravox* has all the right qualities for you. He's debonair, dashing, witty, and yet not too far removed from reality. His down-to-earth Scottish upbringing has made sure that he never forgets his roots, and he is very wary of people befriending him simply because he's well known.

Many of the people he mixes with are very well known, though, and he does like to spend the evening at a club with a circle of friends such as Steve Strange, Bob Geldof, Hazel O'Connor and Phil Lynott.

His flat is beautifully decorated — himself! Smart and sophisticated but natural and friendly, too, there's never a dull moment with Midge around!

Question!

d. In something extremely sophisticated — and bang up to date!

6. Pretty soon, the two of you get chatting. What sort of things d'you talk about?
d. Gossip — nothing malicious but all very interesting!
a. Hobbies, friends and current affairs.
c. Anything and everything — *and* he's a good listener.
b. His work — it means everything to him!

7. If he took you out for dinner, what kind of occasion would it be?
a. A cosy, candlelit affair.
b. A quick snack — food is nothing to make a fuss about.
c. Plenty of egg and chips and beans and sauce, down Frank's Caff!
d. A dinner party with six to eight close friends.

8. What kind of friends does he have?
d. Lots of colourful and successful people, all quite proud of their achievements.
c. Lots of real mates — mostly boys.
b. Only a few, and all quite difficult to get to know.
a. Many acquaintances, all very sophisticated and quite aloof.

9. What would be the main attraction between you?
b. You're both individuals and you're on the same wavelength.
a. You both enjoy a good night out, dancing, talking and laughing.
d. You both look good and together you make an attractive, sophisticated couple.
c. You never need to put on an act for each other — you're just naturally great mates!

Now check to see whether you've chosen mostly a's, b's, c's or d's, then have a look at the conclusions to discover who our mystery men are, and which one's right for you!

If you've chosen an equal number from two sections, it *doesn't* mean that you get two pop stars all to your-self — it simply shows that you don't really go for one particular type of guy!

Mainly a's:
You prefer going out with a guy who is slightly older than you, not because you long for mature and intellectual conversation, but because he'll prob-ably be earning enough to take you to unusual and exciting places! You see yourself as a girl with class and you want to get on in the world, but you're not so ambitious that you're willing to give up having fun!

Your partner will enjoy saving up to take you to a well-known disco in the next town and making a big occasion of it — dressing up, bor-rowing his dad's car, waiting on you hand and foot.

You are both romantics who like to splash out and do everything on a grand scale, but sometimes you may lose sight of the true value of things. It's good that you enjoy letting your hair down, but a shame that you think that the most expensive choice is always the best.

By all means aim high, but don't forget the simpler pleasures of life!

Your mystery partner is none other

than *David Van Day* of Dollar. David is a really nice, genuine guy, but he doesn't mix much with the music business, preferring to spend the evening in upper-class clubs like Tramp and Annabel's. He has great style in clothes and loves champagne and exotic places. An ideal guy for a girl who likes the good life!

Mainly b's:
You like a guy who is very sure of himself, even a little bit arrogant. He is a bit of a contradiction in some ways — he hasn't any time for fuss and ceremony, yet he enjoys attract-ing attention and likes to stand out from the crowd. You like a challenge and therefore you go for a guy who takes a bit of hooking. His hard-to-get act won't put you off, as you like intense relationships, and you don't really go for people who are easy to

get on with immediately.

You are just as opinionated and individual as your guy, which is just as well, or you would soon be trampled underfoot, but this can cause prob-lems, as two very stubborn people are bound to find themselves in deadlock sometimes.

Funnily enough, although you would both refuse to admit to being influenced by anything as superficial as someone's looks, you do pay a lot of attention to your appearance, believing that the way you dress says a lot about your personality.

Because of this, you are ideally suited to *Phil Oakey of the Human League*. Phil really believes in the individual, and does not conform in any way if he can help it. He re-fused to move down to London when the group became famous, saying that he detested London and the music business, and instead, remained in his native Sheffield.

He makes a striking figure, but achieves this simply by putting ordin-ary clothes together in an individual way. He hates discos and eating out, and the friends he has, like him as a person rather than a personality.

91

SO YOU'D LIKE TO GET TO KNOW HIM...?

There's a great art to chatting-up, you know! It's just a shame that most boys don't seem to have learned even the basics! So, what do you do if you're approached by some guy who wants to practise his chatting-up techniques on you? Apart from running a mile, you could always read our Patches guide to the things chatters-up say — we'll prepare you well, we promise!

1. "Want a lift?"
He means: "Jump on the crossbar and I'll pedal like mad."
Don't say: "No thanks! I'd rather walk!" because, if you do, he'll trail along beside you and start doing ridiculous stunts, riding up and down the kerb and on to the pavement in front of you, and you'll never be able to get rid of him.
Best Answer: "OK. I'll wait here while you pedal home and collect your car." That'll make him realise that you're not the sort of girl who's impressed by a twelve-gear push-bike.

2. "You dancing?"
He means: "Would you care to stand opposite me while I throw my arms and legs in different directions?"
Don't say: "With you, do you mean?" in a sneery voice, because then he'll say, "Yeah, this is your lucky day. I've noticed no-one else's bothered to ask you."
Best Answer: "No. It's just a nervous twitch. But I'll try not to embarrass you too much . . ." That should make him back off, immediately. He's blissfully ignorant of the fact that he's making a fool of himself, but he'll be terrified of dancing with someone who might make him look an idiot.

3. "Who's taking you home?"
He means: "I know it's only nine o'clock, but I'm booking my place early. Besides, if we set off now, it'll give me plenty of time to talk about the stars . . . and things . . ."
Don't say: "I'm going home with Sharon," because if you do, he'll go into the kitchen and tell his spotty mate that he's struck lucky — he's found a girl for *him,* too. And Sharon'll never forgive you!
Best Answer: "My big brother and his even bigger dog. The dog's called Dracula, but he's very sweet, really, as long as you don't try to stroke him." Nearly all chatters-up are terrified of dogs, even if they're not terrified of big brothers!

4. "Hey! You with the legs!"
He means: "That's a very nice mini-skirt you're wearing."
Don't say: "Are you talking to me?" because then he'll try to be witty and say something like, "No, I was talking to the caterpillar that's crawling down your sleeve," and before you know it, you'll scream, or laugh, and he'll think he's impressed you with his scintillating humour.
Best answer: Say, "I think that boy's trying to attract your attention, Muriel." Then your friend, Muriel, with the tree-trunk legs'll turn round and give him one of her special seductive stares and embarrass him no end in front of all his mates.

5. "Don't I know you from somewhere?"
He means: "It's the only way I can think of starting up a conversation with a total stranger."
Don't say: "Dunno. Don't think so. What's your name? Maybe you know my brother?" He can play that game for hours, edging closer and closer to you while you try to think of where you've seen him before . . .
Best Answer: "Maybe. If you play ladies' soccer, you might've played against my team." There's a nice little insult in that, and anyway, what chatter-up wants to get mixed up with an expert striker!

As Time Goes By

When you're flicking through your weekly copy of Patches, and you turn to the Help! pages, spare a thought for the girls in Victorian times — some of them were tearing their hair out over problems you'd never even dream of . . .

MOSTLY, readers' letters weren't printed, in order to save space, which meant you'd have to scan through hundreds of answers to find yours. In general, beauty, fashion and careers were the main things which concerned the readers, just as they are today. However, we suspect the answers they got were hardly what they were looking for . . .

UNSYMPATHETIC ADVICE . . .

"Dear Troubled One — We are sorry to hear your complexion is so bad that you are forced to wear a veil over your face. Our doctor suggests you wash your face three times a day with 'Lavender Pimple Soap' and plenty of cold, bracing water. You should see a marked difference within a fortnight. If not, continue with the veils!"

And 'Charlotte' was given a severe telling off when she asked how to darken her hair and reduce her double chin . . .

"To Ungrateful Charlotte — Firstly, if nature intended you to have dark hair, then it would grow that colour! And, secondly, you should be grateful that the hair you complain of does not grow dark on one or both of your chins!" — CHARMING!

And, lastly, a problem which was shared by the majority of fashion-conscious young girls — how to squeeze themselves into a tiny corset without cutting themselves in half at the waist . . .

"What a despicable thing to want to deform yourself for the sake of vanity! How can anyone be attractive when they're doubled in two with pain? Do not waste our time again by writing such nonsense, you wretched girl!"

FASHION

Of course, fashion was as popular a topic then as it is now, so the readers often asked how much they should be expected to pay for clothes, etc.: —
"For the benefit of all our thrifty readers, we've quoted some prices below: —
One pair of long leather boots, £1.1/— (£1.05)
Three full-length dresses, £2.19/— (£2.95)
One year's supply of underwear, 10/- (50p)
One summer bonnet, with silk and lace, 3/- (15p)"

But these were the more expensive ranges for those who earned "a fortune" i.e. £50-£60 a year, as a governess or nanny. However, most of the readers could only dream of owning luxuries like these, as their wage was more likely to be anything between £10 and £18 a year as a ladies' maid, depending on age and background, etc.

And there was no such thing as trotting off to the nearest branch of Top Shop, to try out the latest outfits for the Saturday disco — you either sewed them yourself, or handed them over to the local seamstress to make into modest, ladylike, neck-to-ankle dresses.

And what about casual wear? Well, you might just get away with not wearing your laced corset if you had a very modern mum, but this was rarely the case. And wearing trousers would have caused nothing less than a heart attack in whoever saw you!

BEAUTY

And what about beauty? Well, one thing's for sure — there wasn't exactly an overwhelming range of cosmetics to choose from at the local chemist. In fact, it was only the very "daring" girls who used make-up at all, and even then they had to make their own!

Victorian girls hated freckles just about as much as they detested red hair, and were prepared to do almost anything to get rid of them, usually resorting to the very old-fashioned method of whitening their skin with arsenic and lemon juice.

A mixture of wax melted with berry juice was a cheap recipe for home-made lipstick, and, of course, a set of glowing, white teeth added the finishing touch. We don't recommend you try this nasty-sounding recipe for home-made toothpaste, though . . .

"Take one ounce of powdered charcoal, mix with five drops of quinine and a little rosewater, and brush vigorously for five minutes." (Yeuch!)

All in all, it was suggested that true beauty "came from within," but just think how awful it would be if you couldn't hide behind the warpaint now and again — all the fanciable guys you tried to impress would know exactly what you looked like. (Help!)

THAT'S LIFE . . .

But wasn't life just a tiny bit dull, with no cinemas, no discos and not being able to go off to your friend's party without at least one chaperone hanging about, to see you didn't have too much fun? Well, there was always plenty to do — though, practising your embroidery on a Saturday night, instead of bopping away at the disco, might not seem like a bundle of laughs!

A certain "Miss Lazybones" wrote, saying,
"I left school last year and I am now fourteen. My father pays for all my requirements, so I don't need to work, but I am often bored and don't know how to pass the time each day. What do you suggest?"

"There are plenty of things for a young girl to do. You could read the Bible — it's the best book you could ever look at; and there's cooking, needlework and general house-management to learn, if you are ever to find yourself a decent husband to look after you."

Hmmm, what a lot of exciting things to look forward to . . .

AND FINALLY, BOYS!

There were surely just as many handsome young men going about in those days as there are today, but how did you get to meet them? If you were lucky, you might be invited to the same dinner party, but then it's hardly romantic to be stuck in a crowded room, with ancient great-aunts and uncles discussing the weather for hours on end. So, your best bet was at a friend's party, where you could waltz away the hours (at least until ten o'clock) with the boy of your dreams . . .

No respectable girl would accept a man's offer to see her home, though, and probably the nearest he'd get to a goodnight kiss would be to hold her hand while he begged that she would allow him to see her again.

However, "a daring young girl" got this reply when she asked "if it was rushing things" to expect a kiss on her second date: —

"If you don't mind being talked about behind your back and have no regard for a good reputation, then allow him to kiss you, but if he really cared for you, he would never force you to make this decision so hastily!"

All right, so it may have been romantic, and the clothes were beautiful and the men were gentlemen, but would you really like to swop what you have today — the freedom and chance of a career — for what the Victorian girls had? We know what we'd choose!

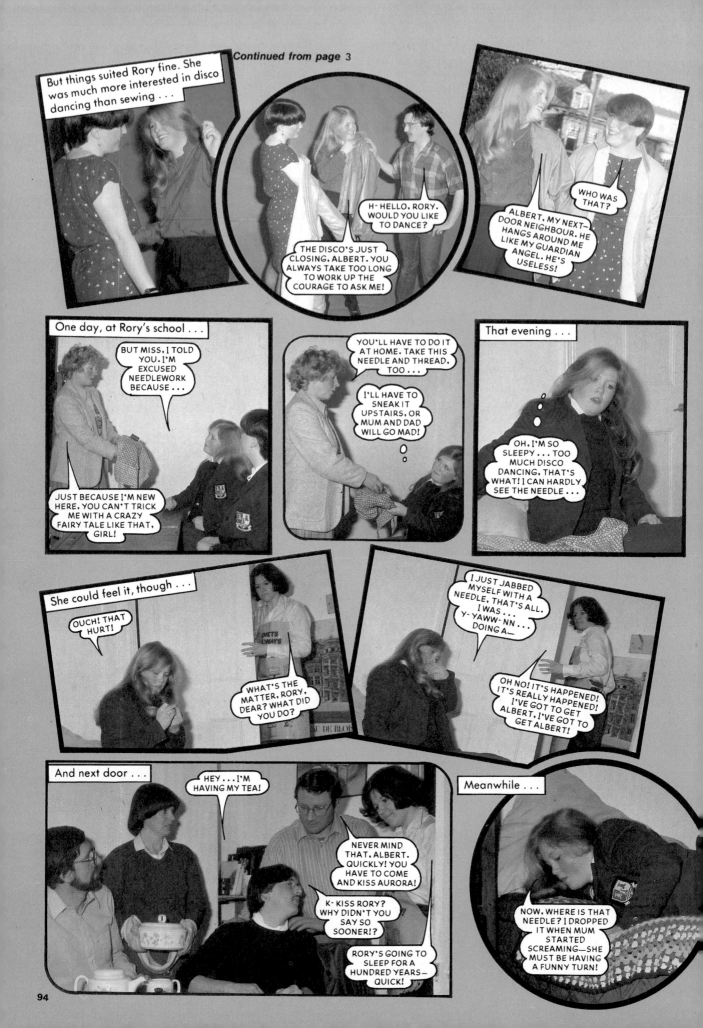